SEX MANNERS FOR

Also by Robert Chartham and available from New English Library:

Confessions Of A Sex Doctor

Sex Manners For Men

Robert Chartham

With a Foreword by
Ralph M. Crowley, M.D.

NEW ENGLISH LIBRARY
Hodder and Stoughton

First published in Great Britain by
Leslie Frewin Publishers Ltd, 1967
Copyright © by Leslie Frewin Publishers Ltd., 1967

First NEL edition 1968
Twenty-fifth impression 1986

British Library C.I.P.

Chartham, Robert
  Sex manners for men
  I. Title

  ISBN 0-450-01176-3

NEL Books are published by
New English Library,
Mill Road, Dunton Green,
Sevenoaks, Kent
Editorial office: 47 Bedford Square, London WC1B 3DP

Made and printed in Great Britain by
Hunt Barnard Printing Ltd., Aylesbury, Bucks.

CONTENTS

Foreword   7

1. The Objective   9

2. Your Equipment ...   17

3. ... and Hers   35

4. The Individual's Response to Sex   46

5. Orgasm, or 'Coming'   56

6. Intercourse   66

7. Two Essentials for Successful
   Lovemaking   92

8. The Well-Mannered Lover and the
   Technique of Lovemaking   105

9. The Well-Mannered Lover on the
   Wedding Night   123

10. The Well-Mannered Lover and His
    Wife's Menstruation   132

11. Impotence   135

12. Objective Achieved?   138

Index   140

FOREWORD

It is unusual to find a sex manual addressed to men only. Even more unusual, perhaps, is to find one that physicians can read with benefit. I hope that this sound manual will reach at least some of the members of the medical profession who need to know more than they do about sexual relations in order to meet fully their responsibilities to their patients.

Three chapters of this book are devoted to good manners in lovemaking. They explain not only what it is important for a man to consider in a woman, but why. This emphasis will be welcomed by psychiatrists who believe that marital troubles often stem from a lack of understanding between husband and wife.

Another wise point of emphasis is Chartham's stress on spontaneity and variety in sexual relations, as well as on the importance of verbal communication. Let go in all ways, he says, and if this means using four-letter words in bed that one might not use elsewhere, then by all means use them. Among such words he includes the word 'love'. The author takes it for granted that the highest satisfactions in sex are impossible unless two people love each other. A lover, he says, may not be a husband, but a husband must be a lover.

Many cherished illusions are contradicted in this book, including the idea that the large penis gives greater sexual enjoyment, an illusion often held by both men and women. Another common to both is that it is the husband's obligation to see that his wife achieves orgasm. The responsibility is shared, Chartham says. He further suggests that it has become a natural part of the male psychology to feel guilty if his partner fails to achieve it. On the other hand, Doris Lessing, who has written several perceptive novels about feminine psychology, claims that it is instinctive for the woman to blame the man for her failure. The psychological problem of how and from whom this illusion originated is still unsolved, but the fact that it is considered here is helpful.

Psychological and psychoanalytical contributions to sexuality are given little place here. The chapter in which their absence is most evident is the one dealing with the individual's response to sex. The author discusses men and women in terms of their sexual capacity: high, average, and low. Yet an individual's sexual capacity cannot be judged as a physical entity, but as a state subject to tremendous variation at different times and with different partners. Even though following fairly consistent patterns, which it most certainly can do, sexual response is still greatly influenced by characterological and emotional factors.

What strikes the reader from the start as a refreshing change from the usual sex manual is the author's personal involvement in his subject. He shares with us those attitudes and values that he has discovered are necessary in the art of successful lovemaking. If he dwells little on the gaps that still exist in our knowledge of sex, or uses little of the recent research on orgasm by Masters and Johnson, he underlines the single most important fact about sex – that our fullest enjoyment of sexual relations as an expression of love is a vital factor in our happiness and well-being. As a corollary to this, Chartham emphasises that there is nothing a man and woman can do in the course of making love that is unnatural or perverted. Fewer patients would consult psychiatrists if they had previously been assured of this truth.

It is in this spirit of liberation that Robert Chartham offers us his knowledge and experience on a subject that is still badly misunderstood.

Ralph M. Crowley, M.D.
Psychoanalyst
Fellow, William Alanson White Institute of
Psychiatry, Psychoanalysis and Psychology
Past President, The American Academy of Psychoanalysis

1 THE OBJECTIVE

Do you know what makes it possible for you to have an erection? Do you know that though she has no penis a woman also has an erection, and in which parts of her body erection occurs when she is sexually excited? Do you know that the average woman requires to be stimulated roughly five times as long as the average man before she reaches orgasm? Do you know that a woman can conceive if you deposit your semen, not in her vagina, but on the outside of the entrance to the vagina? If fact, how much do you know about what makes you and your wife tick in the physical sphere of sex?

In a foreword to my book *Mainly for Wives** an eminent family doctor wrote about the sexual ignorance of women:

> Unless one had first-hand experience of it, it is almost impossible to appreciate the degree of ignorance – abysmal is the only word to describe it – and the fear of practical sex that is encountered in clinics where young wives attend for advice and help because they are childless. Many of these young women have never enjoyed normal intercourse, some, no form of intercourse at all. Until they have plucked up the courage to visit the clinic to seek advice, they have tolerated this situation because either they have had no sex instruction in the early years or the sex instruction they were given was faulty; or other women have told them that 'sex' is just something for men.

' "Sex" is just something for men!' For very many years now this has been the commonly held view. Until comparatively recently girls were given no instruction in the biology of sex, or if some was given it was too rudimentary to be of any practical help.

* *Mainly for Wives* by Robert Chartham, London (MacDonald & Company), 1964.

All too many women went to their wedding night without any idea at all how the sex act was performed. If they had the courage to approach their mothers in an attempt to overcome or at least lessen the nervousness with which they viewed their 'sexual duty' to their husbands-to-be, in ninety-nine cases out of a hundred they would receive the unreassuring reply, 'Don't worry about *that* dear, *he'll* know what to do.'

Indeed, it became a generally held view that every man 'knew what to do,' even if he had not had even one practical lesson from a prostitute before marriage. This idea sprang, I believe, from the fact that a man's basic reaction to his sexual desires and the means whereby he can secure satisfaction are uncomplicated, that he merely had to stimulate the nerves in the tip of his erect penis for two or three minutes in order to produce his climax, and that when he uses a woman for this purpose, all he has to do is to put his penis into her vagina and move it backward and forward until he comes – which he cannot fail to do provided he continues the movements long enough. And this, I fear, is what happened in the great majority of cases. The man made no attempt to help his wife to achieve satisfaction, because he believed she could obtain her climax as easily as he did; and the woman, who very often went through life ignorant of the fact that she could have a climax, accepted the situation and regarded herself merely as the agent whereby the man achieved his satisfaction; in other words, only the man got anything out of sex, and thus sex was only for men; a belief which the man, equally ignorant of his wife's sexual potential, also accepted.

The realisation on a large scale that the woman was capable of climactic sensations similar to those of the man came only about a generation and a half ago, as one fact emerging from the change in sexual-moral attitudes following the First World War and the general movement towards women's emancipation. But the progress of this revolution in the realm of sexual experience was slow, and even at the present time it is all too painfully obvious from the evidence provided by the divorce courts that the men and women who are knowledgeable about practical sex to the extent that they can experience 100 or even 90 per cent satisfactory sex lives are a minority. Statistics show that the main reason for divorce is still sexual incompatibility, not necessarily as the direct cause, but as the source of the general unhappiness, the boredom, the quarrelling, the discontent in the wider field of married life

10

arising out of the physical and psychological tensions built up by unsatisfied sexual desire.

I wrote my book *Mainly for Wives* because I had accumulated evidence that the wife's role in the sex act was still not understood by the majority not only of women, but of men. It is my sincere belief that in the sex life of a married couple both husband and wife have equal responsibilities, and that to have a chance of approaching the ideal, the response to sex must be an equal partnership in which the woman has equal rights with the man. That is to say, she has as much right to achieve orgasm in and, therefore, physical and mental satisfaction from *each* act of sexual intercourse as the man; she has as much right to initiate sexual intercourse as the man; and she has as much right to demand the use of the man's body to achieve her orgasm and satisfaction when she feels the need of it as the man has to require the use of her body whenever he feels the need.

I showed in *Mainly for Wives* how the woman could not only achieve the maximum response to sex for herself, but how, in so doing, she could enhance her husband's experience of sex out of all recognition when compared with the results of his one-sided, aggressive approach to gratification. I pointed out how, if husband and wife did look upon the sexual relationship as an equal partnership, they could bring the lessons in co-operation learned in bed into their wider experience, and to transform, or at least make happier, the whole course of their lives.

I realised that in advocating this approach to sex relations I should undoubtedly encounter opposition, for the aggressive role of the male, which, in his general role as protector of his family, has been carried into the male-female sex relationship over many centuries – at least in the Anglo-Saxon cultures – has influenced the male's overall sexual behaviour so profoundly that it appears to have become instinctive. As little as fifty years ago the woman who believed herself so emancipated that she could initiate the sex act would have been regarded as a freak if not a moral degenerate; despite the fact that the woman's right to more active participation in lovemaking has been recognised by a large number of men, it has not occurred to most of these men that a woman should indicate her desire for sexual intercourse without dissimulation. Even less has it occurred to them that she should, whenever she felt like it, play the active role throughout the act, from foreplay to actual coupling and achievement of

11

orgasm, while the husband lay passive and let his wife have her will of him.

The conditioning of hundreds of years dies hard, as I have said, and this is as true of the woman as of the man. Indeed, the wife's conditioning to the passive role in sexual intercourse is sharply focused in her attitude to sex activity as a whole, which is summed up in the phrase I have already quoted – 'sex is just something for men'. I had, therefore, two barriers to break through: the man's belief in his sexual superiority which makes him the fount of all sex expression, and the woman's acceptance of her own role as the passive agent through whom her husband achieved sexual gratification.

Both these attitudes dominated the Victorian era and have carried over into our own generation; though, since the end of the Second World War, they are speedily being broken down, the number of men and women who are prepared to throw them overboard represent only a very small minority.

The degree of conditioning may be gauged by the effect that attempts to educate both men and women in sex have had on the practice of sex in Great Britain and America. The available list of sex manuals whose object is to explain to both men and women their sexual potential runs into many dozens of titles, and almost without exception, each has sold by the several thousand. Yet even when the number of readers is taken into account it is obvious that these books have exerted a comparatively small influence on sex practice even today.

I personally believe that this has in large part been due to the limitations that the authors have imposed upon themselves in deciding the scope of the information they wished to impart; while the language they have used in an attempt to avoid charges of sensationalism, or indeed pornography, has had the further effect of leaving the reader not far in advance of where he or she started.

To achieve the fullest sexual experience demands a knowledge of how our own and our partner's sexual equipment functions, an appreciation of his or her potential for physical response, and an awareness of the means whereby this potential can be exploited. In other words, it is essential to know the answers to such questions as I asked at the beginning of this chapter, and many more besides.

To return to the other shortcoming of sex manuals besides the incompleteness of the information – namely, the difficulty of the language used. Even a brief study of this aspect of sex manuals

12

reveals that in trying to find language that is neither sensational nor pornographic the authors have obscured what they wanted to say. It is one of the great drawbacks to talking and writing about sex that there is no terminology, for example, for the sexual organs of both male and female that does not involve the actual Latin or Greek terms or the taboo Anglo-Saxon four-letter words. The writer or lecturer must use *penis, vagina, clitoris, testicles, scrotum, semen,* and so on; words which at once inject a certain artificiality into a subject that is essentially real. On the other hand, there are other terms for certain sexual activities which have, in my view, permissible vernacular equivalents. For example, *intromission* means *putting the penis into the vagina,* and I can see no reason why the latter phrase should not be used, though it is five times as long. (I would even use the phrase *inserting the penis* sparingly.) Again, no man alive, I believe, would dream of inquiring of his wife, 'Are you approaching orgasm?' but says, 'Are you coming?' and I can see no objection to using *coming* or *coming off* instead of *approaching orgasm* or *achieving orgasm,* either. It is the overuse of medical or pseudomedical terms which has taken from these books much of their potential value.

But it would be incorrect to suggest that these are the only reasons for ignorance about sex. Most of it stems from the fact that far too many men are only too willing to take the line of least resistance – if one can express it so. This has a biological basis. A man experiences sexual desire, has an erection, and can achieve release from tension, if not complete gratification, by putting his penis into his wife's vagina and moving it about until he comes off – which he may do within a couple of minutes. Though he is clearly not experiencing the height of his sensational potential, he has responded satisfactorily to his urge, and that seems to be all he wants.

I am not speaking academically when I say that the number of those men who are experts in lovemaking is only a very small fraction of those who, as a Frenchman once described them to me, think that 'making love is three thrusts of the buttocks and it's all over'. If such men as these had the knowledge that could turn each session of intercourse into a fresh and exciting experience, I am quite certain that this would be the basis on which they would make love always.

For this is what every act of love should be – a fresh and exciting experience, embarked upon by both partners with the firm intention of extracting the highest degree of physical sensation. The greater the physical sensation the greater is the psychological satisfaction; for each act of sexual coupling is primarily an outward and visible sign of the intangible love which the partners feel for one another. Since the putting of the penis into the very depths of the woman's body provides the closest and most intimate physical contact of which men and women are capable, this act naturally symbolises the closeness of the spiritual contact all lovers crave to make with their loved one.

And there is another important psychological aspect of intercourse. The male actually gives something to the female at the climax of the act – his semen – and the female receives it. For him, therefore, the completed act cannot be anything else than an act of giving. On the other hand, it is not merely an act of receiving for the female, for while she does not inject anything visible or tangible into him, she provides the means for his satisfying not merely his sexual needs, but his necessity to fulfil himself as a male. For a man's sexual prowess is the visible symbol of his ultimate manhood – the reproduction of himself. The combination of the giving and receiving aspects of intercourse, therefore, are superbly symbolic of the essence of love.

But the concept of sexual intercourse divorced from its procreative functions takes this interpretation of sexual intercourse as the expression of a man's and woman's love even further. There is not much point in wanting to express love in some visible form unless the visible form itself takes on a special significance, and this it does when both partners appreciate that to express true love the sex act must itself be as perfectly performed as each has the capacity for performing it. The way to perfection requires a full knowledge of the sexual capabilities of one's own body, and in particular of the sexual potential of each partner.

My objective in this book is to do for husbands what I have done for wives in *Mainly for Wives*. That is to say, I want to lift the husband's response to sex from lust – the satisfying of a purely physical urge in the shortest possible time by the most direct methods – to love – the using of physical sex to express a spiritual urge. This I shall try to do by describing and explaining as fully as necessary what, in my view, a man should know about his and his wife's physical sexual selves.

Before I embark there are one or two points I wish to make clear, to avoid as far as possible the criticism of those who may not fully

14

understand my intentions or approve of a book dealing solely with physical sex.

Having been happily married for more than thirty years, I am fully aware that love entails far more than the satisfactory performance of sexual intercourse. The deep and real love of a man for a woman and a woman for a man means the mutual *total* devotion to each other in *every* aspect of their lives. While I am convinced from my own experience that during their lifetime a man and a woman can love with equal depth more than one partner, I do not believe that any human being can love more than one human being at a time in the way that I have defined love. This love between partners is something very special and very intimate, involving as it does the full sharing of their lives.

But the experience of life is composed of two main ingredients – the physical and the mental – and love must include both if it is to be complete.

I want to stress that it is this understanding of the relationship between love and sex that will underlie everything I shall write about sex in this book, even though from this point on we shall be dealing almost exclusively with practical sex. As I say, I hope, by pointing this out, to forestall any criticism that I place too great an emphasis on physical love by seeming to disregard its mental or emotional aspects.

Finally, I must make clear that I am going to take one or two things for granted. I am going to assume, for example, that you and your wife are physically normally constructed people. So I shall not deal with such questions as sterility, fertility, and frigidity, though I shall have something to say about temporary impotence.

I am also going to assume that you married your wife because you loved her, that you still love her, and that one of the reasons why you have intercourse with her is to experience the 'one person' that a man and woman should try to be.

I am also going to assume that you have decided for yourself your religious and moral attitudes towards sex. If you are not a religious person this side will present no difficulties, and certainly neither religious convictions nor the lack of them will affect the quality of your love for your wife or your approach to lovemaking. If, on the other hand, you are a religious man I would like to draw your attention to one or two observations which I think may be helpful.

The greater part of the enjoyment of living comes from the

15

pleasure provided by the sensations which various parts of the body produce. For example, the pleasure of eating and drinking comes from the taste buds, the pleasure of music and the visual arts by way of the ears and eyes respectively. Such pleasures we accept as natural corollaries of our bodies' functions, and regard the enjoyment of them as a right.

But as God created the parts of your body by which you taste, hear, and see, so He created the parts of your body with which you make love; and as He did so, He implanted in them the means of deriving a physical and mental pleasure quite different from the pleasure derived from other parts of the body, both in the nature and in the intensity of the sensations. Having taken the trouble to do this, He obviously intended that these parts of the body should be used, and used in such a way that the greatest degree of this particular pleasure should be achieved.

There can be no questioning, therefore, of sexual activity between husband and wife and, it follows, no justification for feelings of guilt. In fact, if there is any sin attaching to the sexual activity of husband and wife, it exists only in the feelings of guilt – the feelings of guilt are the sin.

What I have said in these last three paragraphs I regard as of paramount importance, and it is on this basis – love of the partners for one another and the naturalness of sex activity as a bodily function – that I intend to set forth what I maintain you should try to achieve from lovemaking, and how you should make love.

THE VISIBLE MEMBERS

The male's two chief sex members, unlike those of the female, are external and visible. They are the *penis* and *scrotum*. (See figure 1.)

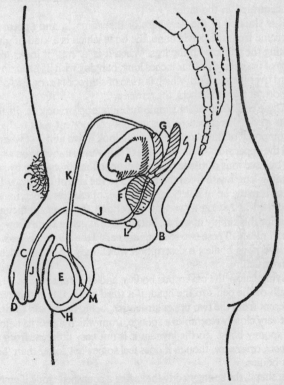

Fig. 1. *The male external and internal sex organs: A, bladder; B, rectum; C, penis; D, foreskin; E, testicle; F, prostate; GG, seminal vesicles; H, scrotum; JJ, urethra; K, spermatic cord; L, Cowper's glands; M, epididymis.*

The penis is the member which plays *the* major role in the whole of the male's sexual experience. In it are the nerves which respond to stimulation by the brain, the eyes, and touch and to the promptings of internal physical conditions (which I shall be explaining presently) by which it changes its size and character from the limp, soft, almost retiring organ whose function is emptying the body of one of its waste products, into the proud, stiff, erect, imperious personification of its owner's sexual nature. In this latter condition it becomes the instrument of both the female's and the male's sexual gratification, by working on the orgasm-producing centres of the former and being the site in which the orgasm sensations are concentrated in the latter.

It is situated at the very base of the stomach, and appears to protrude from the pelvic bone, the bone which is a kind of girdle linking the trunk with the legs. When it is 'at rest' it looks like a tube of flesh three or four inches long, hanging with its head downward over the scrotum, which is a sac of skin containing two other important male members, the *testicles*.

The penis, despite its simple tubelike appearance, is, in fact, quite a complex structure. It is not one component, as it feels, but is composed of three sections. As you look down at it – at what we call the upper side – if the covering of skin were removed you would see two sections of tissue of equal proportions, lying side by side, running lengthwise from the base up to the rim of the head. This tissue is made up of a very large number of cavities which may be described as having a 'vertical direction'. (It is very difficult to describe this simply in words, but a glance at figure 2 will show you what I mean.) These two sections are called the *corpora cavernosa*, or cavernous bodies, a description which may give some idea of their structure.

Lying below the cavernous bodies, and also running the whole length of the penis to the head, is a third section. It is somewhat different from the two upper structures, being composed of tissue that very closely resembles a sponge, from which it gets its name – the spongy body. To the layman it is not very different from the *corpora cavernosa*, though it does feel somewhat softer than those two bodies.

In shape, the spongy body looks like a squashed circle if seen in section. Towards the top of this squashed circle, it is pierced by the urethra, the tube through which the urine passes out of the body, and which, by the planning of an economic Nature, also serves as

18

the duct for the fluid containing the man's reproductive cells or sperm.

Each of the cavernous bodies is pierced by an artery from which an intricate organisation of offshoots supplies blood to the myriad

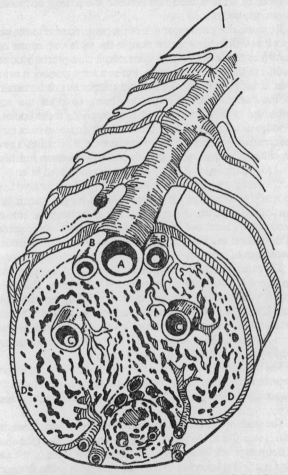

Fig. 2. *Section of the limp penis, illustrating that organ's blood supply. Note how the cavities of the cavernous and spongy bodies are not dilated owing to the absence of blood. A, dorsal vein; BB, dorsal arteries; CC, cavernous arteries; DD, cavernous bodies; E, spongy body.*

19

cells making up the bodies. The spongy body is pierced by two arteries which supply blood to the veins lying outside and on either side of the spongy body and just below the undersurface of the penis and to their accompanying tributaries. There are also a number of veins in the space between the spongy body and the cavernous bodies.

Running along the upper side of the penis, so near to the surface that it is visible through the skin, is the main vein of the organ, known as the dorsal vein. In some men it runs precisely down the middle of the back of the penis, but in a large number it is to one side, either right or left. Two dorsal arteries lie one on either side of the dorsal vein, their function being to assist the arteries imbedded in the cavernous bodies in supplying those bodies with blood, which the dorsal vein draws off and circulates back through the circulatory system by an intricate system of branches. The veins on either side of the spongy body perform the same function for the blood supplied to it by the two arteries imbedded in it.

Without my saying another word, you will have realised that for so small an organ as the penis its blood-supply system is proportionately extremely large. This would certainly be true if the penis always remained limp; but the significance of the great size of the system will become apparent when we come to consider the mechanics of erection.

The penis which you can see is not the whole of the organ. About one-third of its total length is imbedded in the body. This invisible part is known as the root, and is surrounded by muscles that not only hold it in place but join with others, which we shall come to presently, to control the spasms by which the seminal fluid is ejected from the reservoirs where it is stored, all the way along the urethra to the outside of the man's body.

The head of the penis, called the *glans* (the Latin word for *acorn*) because of its shape, is composed of the same kind of tissue as the cavernous bodies. Only a thin layer below the urethra is spongy body.

The shaft of the penis is covered by ordinary skin. Though this skin is sensitive to the touch along the whole length of the shaft, it is not exceptionally so, the reason being that most of the nerves connecting the nervous system of the penis with the general nervous system are concentrated at the lower end of the organ, where it enters the body. In the male at birth the skin of the shaft is extended over the head of the penis in a double layer which allows the fold so formed to be pulled back right to the rim formed by the head where it joins the shaft, to expose the whole top section of the head.

This fold of skin, known as the *prepuce*, or foreskin, is attached to the underside of the head. This small attached piece of skin is called the frenum or frenulum and it is of exceptional importance, for it, and the tip of the penis surrounding the opening of the urethra, is packed full of the most sensitive nerves the male possesses. It is the stimulation of these nerves in lovemaking by the friction of the inside wall of the woman's vagina which eventually brings about the climax.

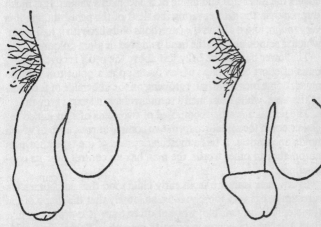

Figs. 3 a and b. *The uncircumcised penis (left) and the circumcised penis (right).*

In certain cultures the foreskin is removed by a simple surgical operation in obedience to religious injunctions, notably among the Jews and Moslems. Circumcision, as it is called, was first enjoined on the Jews by the laws of Moses, and from the very first had a hygienic significance. In the uncircumcised penis various mucous secretions, which flow involuntarily from the penis, collect under the foreskin and pass down to the underside of the rim of the head, where they form a solid substance called smegma. If the foreskin is not regularly pulled right back and the underside of the rim washed to remove the smegma, the latter develops a pungent, distasteful smell and sets up irritation in the penis. Similarly dust or grit from clothing, no matter how careful and clean in his clothing a man may be, penetrates under the foreskin and also sets up irritation unless removed by washing. As will readily be understood, this cannot possibly happen in the circumcised penis, and surely for hygienic reasons circumcision is now a very common operation among non-Jews and non-Moslems in our Western culture. Apart from hygienic reasons, the operation is also performed when the opening of the foreskin is too small to allow it to be pulled back over the head. During circumcision great care is taken not to damage the frenum and its important nerves.

The covering of the head of the penis is not ordinary skin. It is the same smooth, skinlike material (membrane) as that which covers the inner lips and lining of the woman's vagina. It is much thinner than the skin covering the shaft of the penis, though it is very tough, and it allows the cavernous body beneath it to be seen, which is responsible for the head being red or plum-coloured.

The lower part of the belly just above the penis is covered by a mass of short curly hairs which reach up in a point towards the navel. Some men have hairs growing on the underside of the penis at the base, while most men's scrotums have a sparse growth.

The scrotum is a bag composed of two folds of skin joined together down the middle to form two compartments, each of which holds one testicle. It has a muscular system of the type known as automatic; in other words, the man has no control over its contractions.

Every man is aware from early childhood that sometimes his scrotum hangs very loosely, often so loosely that the shape of the testicles is clearly visible; while at other times it is drawn up in a tight bag whose contents seem to be solid. This difference is caused by the contractions of the muscular system. Except when a man suddenly plunges the loosely hanging scrotum into very cold water, whereupon it immediately tightens, he cannot exert any influence upon whether it hangs loose or is tight, nor, except at the sudden application of cold water, will he feel the scrotal muscles contracting. Yet they are in a constant state of movement, for the looseness or tightness of the scrotum has a very important significance and is yet one more example of the truly wonderful construction and functioning of the male sexual system.

As we shall see presently, the male sex cells, the sperm (spermatozoa), are produced by the testicles, and are stored in a tube leading from them but lying inside the scrotum. But sperm, in order to survive, have to be kept at a certain regular temperature.

When this temperature is exceeded, the muscles of the scrotum relax so that the testicles hang down farther away from the body, stretching the skin of the scrotum and allowing the excess heat to escape. If the scrotum is exposed to a colder atmosphere (or cold water), which causes the temperature to fall below the essential level for the survival of the sperm, the muscles pull the testicles up towards the body, where it is warmer, and the skin of the scrotum is automatically made thicker, thus conserving the heat.

When a man is sexually excited, the scrotum is nearly always drawn up tightly. This is the result of the enlargement of the penis in erection and the stretching of its skin which pulls up the scrotum skin to which it is attached. It is not yet medically known whether the interior temperature of the scrotum is affected in this case, but it clearly has no adverse affect on the survival of the sperm, which can, if the need arises, exist for several hours in a temperature higher than their storage temperature.

THE INTERNAL ORGANS

Although the testicles hang outside the man's body, I have included them under *internal organs* because they are invisible and also, and more particularly, they are not joined directly to the penis, but to the whole system of internal organs.

As I have said, the testicles are the sperm factories. Each testicle is egg-shaped, is about one and a half inches long and weighs between half an ounce and an ounce. It is made up of about three hundred tiny, tightly coiled tubes, which if stretched out straight would measure nearly *half a mile*! In these little tubes sperm are produced at a colossal rate, some idea of which can be gained from the fact that the amount of semen normally ejaculated at one coming off – something less than a teaspoonful – contains between 200 million and 500 million sperm.

The sperm differs very considerably from every other cell of the human organism. It has an oval head, a small body, and a very long tail which it thrashes from side to side in order to move itself along, which, when it joins the seminal fluid, it does at great speed in ratio to its size. It is so small that it cannot be seen except under a microscope.

From the testicles the sperm pass, by degrees, into a very long, twisted tube called the *epididymis*, which lies behind the testicles. Here they are stored until the man becomes sexually excited,

23

when they begin to move upward by way of a long, untwisted tube, the *vas deferens*, which is really a continuation of the epididymis.

The vas deferens, some eighteen inches long, runs upward from the testicle within the scrotum, pierces the abdominal wall, and continues up over the front of the bladder and down to the prostate gland which encircles the urethra immediately below the bladder. Just before it does so, however, it spreads out into a small but long bag, called the *seminal vesicle*, resumes its former shape at the exit of the seminal vesicle, pierces the prostate gland, and joins up with that part of the urethra which runs through the prostate. From then on it becomes the urethra.

The seminal vesicles produce a special fluid. As soon as the sperm which have been moved from the epididymis to the seminal vesicles by contractions of the vas deferens, enter this fluid they become frantically mobile. The prostate, which is a gland and muscle combined, also secretes a fluid which joins with the sperm and the fluid from the seminal vesicles as they pass through the gland into the urethra. The combination of these two fluids and the sperm makes what is called *seminal fluid*, or *semen*, the thickish milky liquid that is squirted from the penis when the man comes off. Semen has a characteristic odor, which comes exclusively from the prostatic fluid.

The last of the male's sex organs is a small gland, called Cowper's gland, which is situated in the bulb of the urethra – that part of the urethra which lies just inside the pelvic cavity before it enters the external part of the penis.

This tiny organ typifies, in my view, the miraculous care with which Nature has devised the whole of the male's sexual system. For example, with the exception of the penis, prostate gland, and Cowper's gland, every other organ is duplicated. A man possesses two testicles, two vasa deferentia, and two seminal vesicles; and not only has he two of the organs that manufacture the semen, but each works independently of the other, with the result that if one testicle, one epididymis, one seminal vesicle is damaged beyond repair, the other set is quite capable of producing healthy semen for the successful impregnation of the female egg.

Similarly Cowper's gland demonstrates identical consideration for the most perfect functioning of the penis in intercourse. The outside surface of the head and shaft of the penis when that member first becomes excited is quite dry. If you tried to put it into

24

a woman's vagina in this dry condition and the vagina were also not lubricated, it could cause your partner considerable discomfort. Though when a woman is sexually aroused her vagina is lubricated by the secretion of a gland inside her, Nature was taking no chances that her supply of lubricating fluid might be cut off and implanted Cowper's gland at the base of the penis. A minute or two after the penis becomes erect, Cowper's gland begins to function and secretes a colourless, odourless, slippery liquid which runs up the urethra to its opening and spreads over the head of the penis, thus enabling it to enter the vagina easily even if the woman's lubricating system is not working well.

Here, perhaps, I ought to give a small word of warning. Cowper's gland does not produce the same quantity of lubricating fluid in every man. In some, especially in highly passionate (highly sexed) men, it pours copiously from the opening of the penis almost as soon as full erection occurs. In others, it may not appear for some minutes after erection has taken place, and then may be only a drop or two; some men may think that their Cowper's gland is not functioning because they never see any of the fluid. In such men it does not appear until they are on the point of putting the penis into the vagina; though in a few the gland may not function at all. But there is nothing to worry about if you do not produce much of the liquid or seem to produce none. There is another very efficient lubricating fluid quite handy, which can successfully overcome any deficiency of Cowper's gland – saliva.

This difference in the functioning of Cowper's gland in individual men is not the only difference that may occur. Perhaps the most striking variation can be seen in the penis itself.

The basic form of the penis is the same for all of us, but, like other organs of the body – the nose, the ears, the fingers, for instance – it differs in size from individual to individual. The size of the penis has no relation at all to your general physique. You may be a short, wiry, slim man yet your penis may be long and fat, while that of your friend who is a broad-shouldered, husky strongman may be so small as to be scarcely visible in the midst of its thick surrounding bush of pubic hair.

These are two extremes. Average measurements (as I have said, such measurements have no connection with other body measurements) are as follows. When relaxed, the average-sized penis is 3½ to 4 inches long and 3 to 3½ inches in circumference. In full erection, both these dimensions are increased by little more than one-third, making the average erect penis 6 inches long on the upper side and 4¼ inches in circumference. The large erect penis rarely exceeds 8 to 9 inches in length, and even such examples are extremely rare. There are certainly more penises regarded as smaller than average than larger than average.*

When considering whether a penis is larger or smaller than average, the length is the more satisfactory guide, for a 7-inch penis may have a circumference much less than the 4¼-inch average circumference. Similarly a 5-inch penis can have a 4¾-inch circumference. As we shall see presently, the woman's vagina is capable of stretching sideways and lengthwise to accommodate almost any size of penis, but if any discomfort is caused, it is usually by the length and not the bulk of the organ.

I shall be dealing later with the role of the penis in intercourse and the psychological relationship of the man with his penis, but I want to say here – and I shall probably repeat it – *it cannot be stressed sufficiently that the size of the penis has absolutely no effect whatsoever on the achievement of conception, nor, what is more important to the consideration of our subject here, on the intensity of your orgasm, nor on its capacity to provide your wife with the greatest degree of orgasmic enjoyment and sexual satisfaction.*

* An extremely important discovery, which every man should know about, has recently been made by two American researchers in the field of sex. Dr William H. Masters and Mrs Virginia E. Johnson have measured several hundred penises of all lengths and have reported that it would seem that the longer the penis is in its limp state, the less its length increases proportionately in erection. In other words, the man with the smaller penis, e.g., three and a half inches when relaxed, may have an erect penis of five and a half to six inches, while the man with a five- or six-inch penis in the limp state may have an erect penis of six and a half or seven inches. They report one case of a three-and-a-half-inch penis which increased in erection by 120 per cent to nearly seven and a half inches; and another of four and a half inches with an erect length of seven inches.

This seems to indicate that there are very few penises less than six inches when erect or more than seven and a half inches, a much smaller difference than we had previously believed to exist.

But the great point of this discovery is that it confirms what sexologists have been insisting for a long time – that the man with the small penis should not let the size of his member become a psychological block to his full sexual performance, since physically he is able to provide his partner with the same satisfaction that she would have obtained had his penis been average or larger.

THE SEXUAL NERVOUS SYSTEM AND EROGENOUS ZONES

Erection, the increase in sexual excitement, and the final coming off are all connected with the activity of the sexual nervous system and its interaction on the general nervous system. Other factors are involved, of course, but none of them can do their work if the sexual nervous system is not functioning.

The frenum, the small band of skin attached to the underside of the head of the penis, and the neighbouring area of the tip of the penis are, as I have already noted, supplied with a comparatively large network of nerves which are, at the same time, among the most sensitive in the whole sexual nervous system. The shaft of the

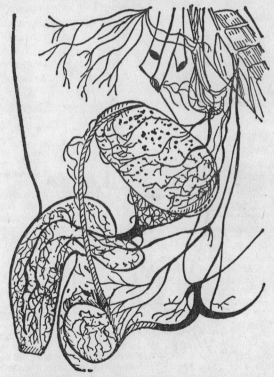

Fig. 4. *The male sexual nervous system.*

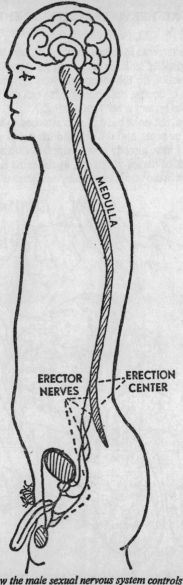

Fig. 5. *How the male sexual nervous system controls erection.*

penis also has a network of nerves connecting the frenum network to a more extensive system at the base of the penis. This network in the shaft is, one might say, merely a simple wiring system, along which the messages from the frenum nerves are carried to the brain and along which the brain's responses are carried back. It is for this reason that the shaft of the penis, though sensitive, is only comparatively slightly so. In other words, if the frenum and tip of the penis are rubbed by a finger, erection will occur within a couple of minutes; if, on the other hand, the whole shaft of the penis is rubbed, even by a completely encasing hand, in movements which avoid contact with the frenum and penis-tip, erection may only occur after five to ten minutes. In fact, a very gentle stroking of the skin of the scrotum, especially toward the back, is likely to bring about erection in a shorter time than stimulation of the shaft of the penis.

From the base of the penis the nerves of the penis – they are called the erector nerves – are connected with the spine at a spot roughly opposite the small of the back. From this erection centre, as it is named, the medulla, the pith of the spine, carries the impulse to erection to an area at the back of the brain, which sends its commands back via the same channels to the blood system and the erectile tissue of the penis, and the remainder of the network of nerves controlling the other sexual organs.

The sexual nervous system is also connected to the nerves of the general nervous system just below the surface of the skin in various parts of the body. Light stroking of the skin of these areas – the so-called erogenous zones – serves to heighten sexual tension and contribute to the eventual intensity of the orgasm.

The man's erogenous zones are the inside of the thighs, his buttocks, which respond to both light and heavy pressure, the small of his back over the erection centre – some men can induce erection merely by stroking this zone alone – his navel, the nape of his neck, his throat, and behind his ears. His lips are also sensitive if sucked or the tongue explores the inner surfaces.

The response to caresses in these zones varies from individual to individual. In some men there is greater sensitivity in, say, the inner thighs, while there are many who appear to have been provided with extra zones. The majority of men have no response to caressing or sucking of their nipples, but there are some lucky ones who declare that they have the greatest erotic reaction in this area. I have known at least three men who could bring themselves off by rubbing their nipples between fingers and thumbs. I believe this to be rather rare, but it is a fact that if there appears to be no erotic sensation in the nipples it can be induced. In the majority of men the nipples tend to be undeveloped physically, lying almost flush with the surrounding areola. It is in these cases that erotic sensitivity is most likely to be lacking, for the men who claim an erotic response from their nipples have well-developed ones standing out from the areola. It is possible, however, to develop the nipples so that they stand out by devoting a short time daily to pulling them outward and kneading them between finger and thumb. After a time they will come to have a degree of erotic response which is well worth the trouble. There are also some men who find that they have their greatest erotic response – outside the frenum and penis-tip – to light caresses on the base of their bellies in the area of their pubic hair and just above. Again I have known men who claim that they can achieve erection merely by light stroking of this zone, though there are many others who are completely unresponsive there.

ERECTION

The phenomenon of erection is, in my view, among the most wonderful of the many wonderful aspects of a man's sexual functioning. The change of the penis from the limp, soft, friendly, retiring appendage into a decidedly larger, stiff, erect, bold, proud and imperious organ, which seems almost to have a personality of its own, is surely one of Nature's greatest miracles.

The physical change is brought about by blood pouring into the thousands of cavities which honeycomb the cavernous and spongy bodies of the penis. There is, of course, always a certain amount of blood in these cavities, but as soon as the brain transmits its commands to the erector nerves, these in turn stimulate the blood system of the penis which pours blood into the cavities, causing them to swell until the whole organ is enlarged to its greatest capacity and is erect and hard. When the penis is limp the rate of inflow and outflow of blood into and out of the cavities is equal; in erection the rate of inflow is far more rapid than the outflow, causing the cavities to remain engorged and swollen until the urge for relief from sexual tension abates either by coming off, or by directing the mind to nonsexual things, which, though possible after long practice, is not easy to achieve.

A Danish book about sex which was recently published in

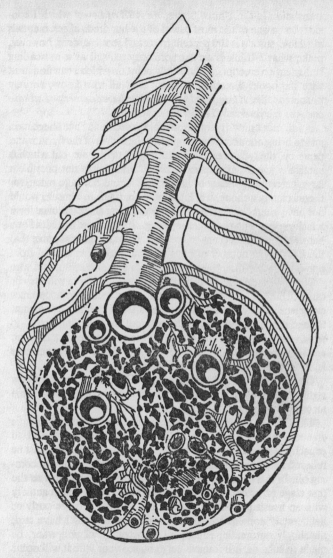

Fig. 6. *Section of the erect penis. Note how the cavities are swollen with blood, thus causing the penis to increase in size and become hard.*

translation in the United States, *An ABZ of Love*,* which I consider to be one of the most useful of the hundreds of sex manuals available, since it is 100 per cent frank and sensible, does, however, make what I think is an extraordinary as well as a misleading statement on erection. It is the only point on which I can find fault with the book. 'Erection,' it says, 'is as all men know, entirely uncontrollable. *It is impossible to decide to have an erection and have one – or the reverse.*' (The italics are mine.)

As all men know, it is quite possible to decide to have an erection and to bring one about by stimulating the nerves of the frenum and penis-tip, the type of erection which I call deliberate, but which is medically known as a reflex erection. If this were not possible a large percentage of acts of intercourse would not take place, for there is many a thoughtful husband who, if left to himself, would not have intercourse on a particular occasion since the urge for it is lacking, but who nevertheless, recognising his wife's need, allows her to stimulate his penis to erection. I should imagine, too, that there is a large number of boys who masturbate as a relief from boredom rather than to seek relief from sexual tension, and who deliberately stimulate their penises to erection. There will also be quite a number of middle-aged and older men who sometimes experience a condition – sometimes called temporary impotence, though it is not impotence at all (as I shall be explaining later) – in which they have a strong desire for sexual activity but have no erection until the penis is deliberately stimulated. This experience is, in fact, an extraordinarily common one.

On the other hand, the authors of *An ABZ of Love* are absolutely right when they say that a man cannot prevent himself from having an erection if his sexual system says he is to have one.

There are, in fact, two main types of erection. There is automatic erection, which occurs when the seminal vesicles are full to capacity. This fullness triggers off a sexual tension which must be relieved by emptying the vesicles of semen by ejaculation at coming off. In this case, the penis automatically becomes erect as the first stage of sexual excitement, prompting you to sexual activity with an irresistible force. In this case, nothing is consciously or deliberately done to stimulate the erection. It is, as I have said, absolutely automatic; it can, by the exertion of willpower, be made to subside, but immediately you see your wife it will occur

* *An ABZ of Love* by Inge and Sten Hegeler, translated by David Hohnen, New York (Medical Press of N.Y.), 1963.

again and persist until you have made love and come off; or, if you are temporarily parted from your wife, as soon as you go to sleep and cease to have conscious control over it, the erection will recur and tension build up until you have an involuntary orgasm and ejaculation, familiarly known as a 'wet dream'.

The other main type of erection is brought about by a kind of reverse process from the one I have just described. Besides producing sperm, the testicles also produce hormones which reach the brain via the bloodstream and, so to speak, eroticise it. In other words, the action of the hormones on the brain induces sexual desire by stimulating the recollection of stored memories either of sexual acts previously indulged in, or dreamt of, or consciously desired. As a result, the brain becomes crowded with erotic images, which set up an excitement, which in turn is transmitted to the erector centre. As soon as the excitement or tension reaches a certain pitch, the seminal vesicles produce their fluid at a greatly increased rate, become full to capacity within a very few moments, and add their demand for relief to the general sexual tension.

Exactly the same results are achieved not by crowding the brain with erotic images as a first stage to excitement, but by the close proximity or touch of your beloved partner and the opportunity for lovemaking. I think it must be in the experience of all of us that sometimes we go to bed without any conscious intention of an urge to make love, but as soon as we put an arm about our partner, a hand on her breast, or feel her thighs against ours, we experience an onrush of sexual desire and before we quite realise what is happening to have an erection. It has not yet been discovered whether unconscious erotic images stimulate the hormones secreted by the testicles to produce the effect on the brain and sexual system that I described in the last paragraph, or whether unconscious erotic images can have the same effect on the sexual system with the help of the hormones. In any case, the overall effect is the same; there will be no relief from the tension until you have come off.

There is also a type of erection which has no sexual significance whatsoever. Practically every man has awakened in the morning to find that he has an extremely strong erection. He has probably been sleeping on his back which has brought about pressure on the nerves in the erection centre. It soon subsides; although naturally, by an association of ideas – erect penis plus sexual thoughts, for example – a mechanical erection may lead to a genuinely sexual erection. This being so I must issue another warning: there is some risk of organic damage being caused if a morning erection, in particular, is used to enjoy stimulation and activity to orgasm, either by intercourse or masturbation, because the spasms of the muscles producing the orgasm and ejaculation may exert their pressure on a possibly swollen bladder already in high tension. If you want to have intercourse before getting up – and there is much to commend it, as I shall be describing later – you should empty your bladder before embarking on it. Though urinating will cause the penis to subside, the process of subsidence is a slow one and the penis will still be quite swollen if you return to bed immediately from the bathroom. In this swollen state the frenum nerves are much more susceptible to stimulation than when the penis is quite relaxed, and only a second or two's attention will be enough to restore the erection to its full strength.

Finally, some men experience a mechanical erection which may safely be transformed into a genuine sexual erection. Erection comes about quite spontaneously, and, indeed, unconsciously, when the man lies on his side with his legs together and his knees drawn right up to his stomach so that the testicles as well as the penis are pressed firmly between the upper thighs and the pubic area. Most of the pressure exerted is on the scrotum, and its nerves appear to communicate, under this pressure, with the erector nerves. Erection will not occur unless this pressure is put on the scrotum, and there will be no pressure on the scrotum if, for example, it is pushed backward to the rear of the thighs so that it appears behind the legs. As I have said, not all men can induce erection in this way, though many more can do so than are aware that they can.

The information I have given in this chapter will, I hope, help you to understand better than you did before how you function sexually. My ultimate aim in this book is, as I have said previously, to show you how to gain from coming off not only the maximum voluptuous sensations at the peak of the climax, but the greatest relief from tension and therefore the highest degree of physical and mental satisfaction. For your own general happiness this is necessary; but even if you achieve it, this happiness can be greatly enhanced if you can help your partner to obtain a similar satisfaction herself, and for this you should know as much about how she functions as you do about yourself. For this you must have a general idea of her equipment.

34

Though two of your wife's sex members are external – the clitoris and the outer lips of the vagina – unlike your penis and scrotum they cannot ordinarily be seen; so in effect one may say that all the woman's members are invisible, while the most important so far as you are concerned for the achievement of your sexual satisfaction – her vagina – is internal.

The vagina is the counterpart of the penis. As its name implies (*vagina* is the Latin word for *sheath*). It is an inlet in her body designed to take the penis as a sword-sheath takes a sword. It goes up into the body from an opening situated in her at the same spot as your penis is attached to you – at the point where the trunk joins the legs. (See figure 7.)

The average normal vagina is between 3½ and 4 inches long, but it has an elasticity which allows it to stretch both sideways and lengthwise so that it may accommodate any size penis. The walls of the vagina consist of very delicate membranes which are the same type as that covering the head of the penis. These membranes have such qualities that they react on the sensitive nerves in the frenum and penis-tip when the latter are moved against them; and, in effect, it is they which are responsible for building up the tension in your sexual system which, when at its height, brings about the muscular spasms that force the semen out of the penis.

At the far end of the vagina is the cervix, or neck of the womb. The womb, in which the fertilised egg develops into a baby, is a hard, almost bonelike, hollow, pear-shaped structure. The neck is what would be the top of the pear and in it is an opening from the vagina into the interior of the womb, by which the sperm enter in search of the egg. In the unpregnant woman the womb is about three inches long, but it has the most extraordinary expansive qualities, which allow it to swell to many, many times its normal size as the developing baby grows. While the womb in general plays little part in the woman's experience of lovemaking, the cervix does, as will be seen later.

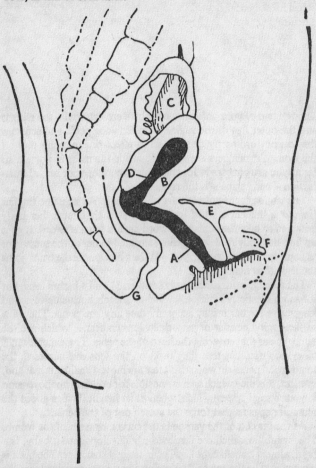

Fig. 7. *The female internal sex organs. A, vagina; B, womb; C, ovary; D, cervix, or neck of womb; E, bladder; F, clitoris; G, rectum.*

The other internal parts of the woman's sexual system, which we are also not concerned with since they play no part in lovemaking either, are two sets of ovaries, which hold the eggs; the follicles, which surround the eggs and burst when an egg is ripe, thus releasing it; the Fallopian tubes, in which the egg waits to be fertilised by the male sperm and down which it moves into the womb, either when it has been fertilised or has ceased to be capable of fertilisation and must leave the body during menstruation to make way for the next mature egg.

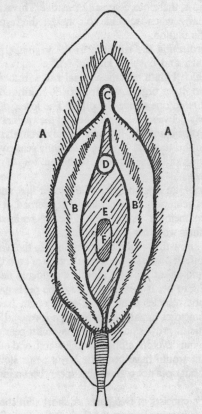

Fig. 8. *The female external sex organs. AA, large lips; BB, small lips; C, clitoris; D, urethra; E, intact hymen (in virgins); F, interior of vagina.*

We must now return to the external organs which, with the

vagina, play the major role in the woman's experience of stimulation and coming off. (See figure 8.)

The opening of the vagina is covered and protected by two folds of flesh known as the outer, or large, lips and the inner, or small, lips, and it will be noted that besides being smooth and pink, their covering has a different texture from ordinary skin. This covering is the same membrane that lines the vagina and covers the head of the penis, and is, therefore, especially sensitive. This sensitivity will loom quite large when we come to consider the response of the woman to stimulation.

Besides protecting the entrance to the vagina, the small lips extend upward and cover a kind of 'ridge' above the vaginal entrance, which I shall call the vaginal ridge. Imbedded in this ridge are two other organs which I briefly mentioned just now. They are situated one above the other. The lower one, which is about midway between the upper one and the vaginal entrance, is the opening of the urethra, the tube leading from the bladder. In some women this urethral opening is sexually sensitive; that is to say, stimulation of it can contribute to the build-up of the woman's sexual tension.

The upper organ is in the apex of the inner lips, and insofar as the woman's achievement of orgasm is concerned, it is her most important sex member, as the ancient Greeks realised when they called it by their word for 'key' – clitoris.

You may know that as the baby develops in the womb, for the first few months it possesses the sexual organs of both the male and female. Round about the fifth month it suddenly decides which sex it is going to be. If it is to be a boy, the penis grows rapidly larger and the testicles come down what might have been the vagina, which closes up, and the scrotum is formed. If it is to be a girl, the testicles grow smaller until they disappear completely, while the vagina develops along with the womb and other internal organs. What would have been the boy's penis slows down its growth rate, but does not entirely disappear, becoming the clitoris instead.

The clitoris consists of two parts. A short slim shaft about an inch in length is embedded in the flesh at the top of the vaginal ridge and is covered by the small lips, and though it can be felt, it is completely out of sight. This shaft ends in a head which emerges above the flesh and, if large enough, can be seen. Both shaft and head correspond exactly to the structure of the male penis, so that, except for the fact that the urethra does not pass through it, and it has, therefore, no opening, it is to all intents a miniature penis. The head is even protected by a foreskin.

It is in the head of the clitoris, as in the head of the penis, that the woman's most sensitive sexual nerves are situated. Stimulation of the head of the clitoris will cause all the other sexual nerves to become excited and build up tension that can only be relieved by the woman coming off.

Besides these primary sex organs, as they are called – the clitoris, inner and outer lips, and vagina – the woman also has secondary sex organs, namely, her breasts. The woman's breasts are much more closely connected with her sexual nervous system than are the male's with his. Indeed, they are the organs which come next after the clitoris in their ability to stimulate her whole sexual system. To illustrate this, while the most common method of female masturbation is rubbing the clitoris with the finger, very many women can bring themselves off or be brought off by fondling or sucking the nipples.

I can almost hear you asking: But what about the action of the penis in the vagina? Surely that is a major source of stimulation?

It is a misunderstanding of this point which has been largely responsible for so many women in the past not realising that they were capable of orgasm, and of too many rarely experiencing orgasm today. For the fact is that though the sensation of the penis in the vagina is an essential accompaniment to the other stimulation if the greatest sensation is to be obtained at coming off, there are very few women indeed who can be brought to climax by friction of the vaginal walls alone. Even then, the sensation of the penis in the vagina has a more psychological than physical significance for the woman. Without it the giving-and-receiving aspect of the act would be lost. This is also partly true of the man's experience of the penis in the vagina, though the physical sensations are notable for him.

The majority of women unless they are directly stimulated at the clitoris will not come off; from which it is not illogical to maintain that the clitoris is the chief seat of the woman's erotic experience. When I am later dealing with the technique of foreplay, you will realise how important the role of the clitoris is. For the moment, I would like to make one point in this connection to underline what I have said about direct stimulation of the clitoris *in some form* being essential to the woman's attainment of orgasm. There is little doubt that when the human species was developing from the primates, the clitoris was so placed that when the penis entered the vagina the base of the upper side rubbed against it and stimulated the woman to orgasm during the movements of intercourse. It may have been the uncertainty about the correct source of orgasmic response that gave rise to the theory of vaginal orgasm.

The number of modern sex manuals that still specifically describe this penis-clitoris friction as an essential part of coupling and maintain that through it the woman comes off is as surprising as it is misleading. For the fact is that only a very small proportion of women are built with a clitoris located in such a way as to come in contact with the penis as it thrusts into the vagina. The couple who do experience clitoris-penis contact naturally are lucky indeed.

The siting of the clitoris is not the only part of the woman's sexual equipment to experience modification. Just as the penis, though always conforming to the basic shape, differs from male to male in length and bulk, so the positioning of the vaginal entrance is different from woman to woman.

Unfortunately, there is no record of the stage in his development that Man adopted the face-to-face-lying-down method of coupling instead of the rear-entry method used by the primates from which he evolved. It must have been several millennia ago, because the positioning of the vaginal entrance has become so modified that in most women it presents itself most readily to the man's penis when he places himself between his wife's legs facing her. Nevertheless there is still a very small number of women in whom the outer and inner lips are situated so far back that front entry is extremely difficult, while rear entry presents no difficulty at all. The actual positioning of vagina entrance varies so much from woman to woman that a man with wide sexual experience knows that he has to modify his technique for each woman with whom he couples. Not that these modifications are necessarily very great, but one exact pattern of coupling is rarely right for any two women. I shall be referring to this again, because it plays an important part in technique, and from my experience I have found that very few men realise there are these physical variations in women.

The last of the female sex organs we need to consider are the Bartholin glands which correspond to the male's Cowper's gland. The Bartholin glands are situated just above the entrance to the vagina, and as soon as sexual tension reaches a certain pitch they begin to pour out a fluid which lubricates the entrance to the vagina, thus helping the penis to enter without discomfort.

This is, however, not the only source of the woman's lubrication, and this second source is somewhat of a mystery to the medical profession still. The mystery lies in the fact that although the walls of the vagina contain no secretory glands whatsoever, within fifteen to twenty seconds of the woman's becoming even ever so little sexually excited, the vaginal walls begin to produce a lubricating fluid. The production of this fluid precedes the production of fluid from Bartholin's glands by some time.

And one final observation: The pubic bone of the woman is covered by a thick layer of fat, which gives it a rounded appearance that has resulted in its being called the Mount of Venus. The mound, like the man's pubic bone and lower belly, is covered with a mass of thick, short, curly hair. This mass of hair differs in shape from the man's pubic hair, for whereas his goes upward in a point toward his navel, hers has a straight line across the top, giving it the general appearance of a triangle pointing downward.

THE SEXUAL NERVOUS SYSTEM AND THE EROGENOUS NERVES

Whereas the man's response to sexual stimulation is concentrated mainly in his penis and scrotum up to the point of orgasm, the woman's is much more diffused. This is the result of her sexual nervous system not being concentrated in the area surrounding her most sensitive sexual nerves – her clitoral nerves – but spread extensively throughout her whole body. It is not necessary to go into a full description of the woman's sexual nervous system here, as I did with yours in the previous chapter; a good example of what I mean is provided by the direct connection of the nerves of her breasts – through the spinal column – with the nerves of the clitoral and vaginal areas.

Another indication of this greater diffusion of sexual nerves is the greater number of erogenous zones the woman possesses compared to the man's; even where these correspond, they are generally much more sensitive to stimulation. One of these erogenous zones is at the backs of the knees and along the inner thighs; you can do much to arouse a woman by running your hand very lightly over the back of one knee, around her inner thigh, over to the other inner thigh and down to the back of the other knee. If you then retrace this path, you can keep up a constant stimulation.

Another erogenous zone is the actual opening of the vagina. This responds to the gentle in-and-out pressure of the finger or thumb, but much more to the attention of the head of the penis. I propose to leave full consideration of these zones, including the clitoris, to a later chapter on the technique of foreplay.

A woman responds, as you do, to light caresses with the palm of your hand over her Mount of Venus and her belly, while some women find tickling of the navel with the tip of the tongue especially exciting, though for others it may have just the reverse effect. Stroking of the breasts with the palm of the hand brings a response from all women, and the large majority are also responsive to caresses on the shoulders, throat, nape of the neck, and behind the ears, while explorations of the tip of your tongue on her inner lips all add to the build-up of tension. The whole length of her spine is as sensitive as yours, though she has no erection centre. In fact, many more parts of her are capable of erection, and for the same cause – of engorgement – compared with your one erectile member, the penis.

ERECTION

When a woman comes off, she does not, like you, have a corresponding ejaculation. This was only finally discovered early in this century, and up to this time it was thought that women did ejaculate. What was mistaken for this was a slippery substance which is secreted by the inner membrane of the womb and flows towards the opening of the womb, closing it up like a plug. At the peak of orgasm the contractions of the womb force this 'plug' through the opening into the vagina, which, already moist with the lubricating fluid, now becomes overcharged with liquid, sometimes to the extent that it flows out of the vagina. The passing of the 'plug' through the opening of the cervix also gives the woman, or at least some women, the sensation that she has discharged something.

Once again I must point out that the amount of the slippery substance secreted by the womb varies from individual to individual. In some it is not sufficient to form a 'plug', and when this is so the sensation of ejaculation is absent, though often the contractions of the cervix are mistaken for this.

42

When you begin to apply stimulating caresses to a woman, her nipples are the first to respond. They swell, stand out from the areola, and become hard. After continued stimulation the gradual build-up of tension is communicated to the clitoris. As would be expected on account of its similarity to the penis, the clitoris swells and hardens. When the woman is not sexually excited the shaft imbedded in the flesh cannot be felt; under stimulation it can be felt quite easily, while the head is pushed out of the protective covering of its foreskin so that it presents itself for caresses of the finger, tongue, or penis.

Almost simultaneously with the erection of the clitoris the inner lips swell and open. The Bartholin glands begin to produce their libricating fluid, and by this time the rim of the vaginal entrance will also have swelled, presenting a larger and easy opening for the penis to enter.

I purposely delayed until this point giving a detailed description of the construction of the vagina, since here, too, erection occurs. The wall of the vagina is made of three layers, the one touched by the penis being, as I have said, not ordinary skin but a mucous membrane. This membrane has many folds in it which allow it to expand to take a penis of any size and to reach its fullest extent when the baby is being passed from the womb to the outside world at childbirth. Thus, no matter what size penis is put into it, its walls still have a number of folds in it. These folds are partly responsible for the friction of the nerves of the penis, but the build-up of tension during actual coupling is brought about by the friction of the penis nerves by a large number of ridges on the vaginal walls.

The middle layer of the vaginal wall is a spongy body, not unlike the spongy body of the penis. This spongy body is well supplied with blood vessels which, under sexual stimulation, cause it to swell, thus bringing about what may be termed erection of the vagina. This vaginal erection not only adds the stimulation-reaction of its network of nerves to the woman's sexual nervous system as a whole, thus helping to increase the build-up of tension, but, by its cushioning effect, protects the inserted penis from discomfort when the muscles, which form the third and outer layer of the vaginal walls, contract as the woman comes off. Therefore, instead of the penis, which will be near the apex of its tension at this time, being gripped by a hard surface, which could have the effect of destroying the greater part of the man's voluptuous sensations at this time, it is gripped by a soft, undulating cushion which greatly increases the total sex-tension and the voluptuous experience.

To recapitulate briefly, then: The woman is capable of erection in at least five of her sexual organs compared with your one. She has what may be termed a true erection, since it is entirely identical with the erection of your penis, in her nipples and clitoris, both of which increase in size and harden. The swelling of the inner lips, the rim of the vagina, and the vagina itself, though not producing hardness, nevertheless causes these parts to become more prominent, and since it is brought about also by engorgement of blood, can rightly be called erection.

As your penis becomes much more responsive to stimulation when it is erect, so these erectile parts of the woman become much more sensitive. This is another reason why the woman's response to sexual tension is much more widely spread throughout her body than is yours.

There are several differences between your reaction to sex and a woman's. I shall be dealing with some of these presently, but there is one major difference which I must refer to here.

As I said in the last chapter, erection of the penis is the indisputable sign of sexual tension in the male. I also described the chief types of erection: the deliberate erection caused by the direct stimulation of the nerves of the penis-tip and frenum; the automatic erection over which the man has no control and which is brought about by the overcharging of the seminal vesicles that in turn stimulate the brain to produce erotic images and thoughts. These thoughts and images stimulate the sexual nervous system to ever-increasing activity until the tension is built up to such a pitch that relief can only be achieved by coming off.

The woman experiences automatic erection much less frequently than the man, which is understandable since she has no equivalent of the seminal vesicles and their characteristics. When she does have an automatic erection, which is nearly always preceded by an upsurge of initial stirrings in the sexual nervous system, it is usually just before or just after menstruation, and though the reason for this is not yet fully understood, it clearly has something to do with the biological changes taking place in her sexual system at that time. However, she is also capable of automatic erection from other causes, which are entirely psychological in origin, but in which, as opposed to the man, erotic images play

44

little, if any, part in the initial stages.

As you know without my telling you, the sight of a beautiful woman, particularly in the nude, is quite enough to give you a spontaneous automatic erection. Your mind is at once filled with erotic thoughts and images in which you imagine yourself caressing and making love to the girl with the ultimate intention of intercourse and orgasm. In these imaginary encounters your whole experience will always be perfection. You will respond to her kisses and caresses, you tell yourself, as you never responded before, and when you come off you will swoon with the voluptuous sensations of it. And – probably far more important – you will make her experience something she has never had before, and you will bring her off with such intensity that she will come back again and again for more. This is the train of your thoughts whether you are conscious of it or not; and in reacting in this way you will be reacting quite normally, for, because of the ease with which he can be roused and the speed at which he can come off, Man is by nature a promiscuous creature. On the other hand, if you are married and have mastered the technique of lovemaking which makes coupling with your wife a perfect or near-perfect experience on nearly every occasion, though you will still be affected by the sight of a beautiful woman, your thoughts will transfer themselves to the object of final intimacy in your actual everyday life – your wife.

You will know, too, that statues and pictures of nude women can have almost as an intense effect on you as a live nude female body; as likely as not, you have been roused to erection and tension by descriptive passages in books. This, also, is a natural male reaction.

The woman, on the other hand, is very rarely stimulated by the sight of a beautiful nude male body, either in the flesh or in pictures or in a statue; and though she may occasionally be stirred by what she reads, it is only occasionally. What rouses her is direct stimulation in the form of caresses. Once roused, however, there are a number of physical contacts to which she responds that are outside your range of experience, all of which we shall be considering in due course.

For the time being, may I ask you to consider very carefully what I have written here in this chapter, because it contains some of the basic knowledge on which the technique of lovemaking is founded.

'She's a hot little piece!' we sometimes say when a girl exhibits a frank, eager, and uninhibited response to our sexual advances, knowing that if we took her to bed we would have a really passionate hour of lovemaking. Far more often, however, we sense that if we could get a girl to sleep with us, she would consent not because she wanted us sexually – to use our bodies to satisfy a sexual tension demanding release – but because she was bored or insecure, and craved excitement or reassurance of some kind, and the resulting experience would be nothing to savour or gloat over.

There is an admiration in our description of the first girl which derives from the fact that, as men, we set great store by our own virility and our degree of sexual potency – the capability of sustaining a really stiff erection for sufficient time, and more, to bring a woman off satisfactorily no matter how long she may take. The claims of Casanova are the expressions of the dream world in which the majority of us live sexually.

The fact remains, however, that there are some men and women who are far more active sexually than others, and some who are far less sexually demanding than others. Indeed, there is scarcely one individual whose sexual requirements are exactly identical with another's.

Broadly speaking, however, there are three main groups of men and women distinguishable by their sexual demands and activity. First, a comparatively small group of what we term highly sexed, or highly passionate men and women; second, an extremely large group of average-sexed men and women; and a third group, again smaller, but not quite so small as the first group, of men and women who experience sexual tension only infrequently – the low-sexed.

The medium-sexed, who, because of the preponderance of their numbers are taken to represent the norm, may be said roughly to experience sexual desire, arousal, and the need to come off two or three times a week (in their twenties, a weekly average of four to five times). The low-sexed may experience sexual desire, arousal, and the need for orgasm only once every two weeks or once a month. The highly sexed, on the other hand, have at least a daily urge, often a twice-daily or thrice-daily urge.

That there are men and women who not only have the urge, but who make love to orgasm two or three times a day, is a fact, and they are not boasting or exaggerating when they make such a claim. The majority of them keep their sexuality under some degree of control, but I suppose most of us have met one or two men who do not attempt to conceal their interest in sex, an interest which appears to be the most important thing in their lives, so that we may say they are obsessed by sex. I have a shrewd suspicion, too, that unless we are one of them, we tend to disapprove of them because of their high sexuality, just as we are apt to *pity* the man who clearly has a much smaller interest in sex than our own, and whose sexual experience is on a lower level than ours.

Unconscious sexual jealousy provokes our disapproval of the highly sexed, but our pity for the low-sexed derives from our tendency to take a man's response to his sexuality as a yardstick for measuring his manhood. In primitive times, and among some primitive tribes even today, the man who produced a large number of sons was highly respected, because he thus demonstrated that he possessed the vital spark of manhood in his loins. In many ancient religions sex was adored and worshipped over and above any other object of veneration, initially because, though men associated their own ability to reproduce themselves with the penis, they did not understand the mechanics of reproduction – and what they did not understand they worshipped – and later, because having come to an appreciation of their reproductive power, they believed they must propitiate the god who bestowed it, lest, not valuing this super-mortal and superlative gift as highly as they should, they should be deprived of it. The power of sex dominated our early ancestor's whole conception of the world, and since he possessed in his own seed the miraculous gift of life itself, all that was vital in life he designated male. The vigour of the sun, fire, heat, the sowing of the seed were male; the moon, water, cold were female. Under the influence of the sun's warmth the earth, The Great Womb of Nature, The Great Mother of God, welcomed the seed; and out of this basic conception of the male and female roles emerged the concept that the earth (the female) would be barren and cold without the vitalising attentions of the sun and the seed. Though some ancient religions included in their worship of sex a representation of the vagina (the *yoni*), all regarded an image in stone or wood of the phallus – the erect penis – or some symbolic resemblance of it, as the main form in which sex could be most powerfully portrayed visually. It is from this very ancient assessment of the male's sexual power that we get our own modern view of the male's sexual superiority, and hence the evaluation he sets on his ability to satisfy the female; in other words, his virility or potency, the hardness of his erection and his capacity for sustaining it, all of which is connected with the actual size of his penis, though this concern with the dimensions of the phallus is subconscious in most men.

That we are provoked to envy of the highly sexed and to despise the inferior sexuality of the low-sexed derives from our ignorance of the nature of the sexual urge and the varying degrees of sexuality which different people possess. In fact, the nature of their sexual urge is as valid a characteristic of a man or a woman as are blonde hair, brown eyes, a flat belly, beautiful breasts, an artistic or non-artistic appreciation, a bad temper, a disposition to gaiety, a quick wit. It is an essential component of our total make-up, and can no more be ignored or changed (though it can be controlled, if control is necessary and there is a willingness to be strong-minded about it) than can any other physical characteristic.

What it is in our general physical make-up that determines the strength of our sex drive (sex urge, response to sexual tension) is still a subject of some controversy among sex physiologists and psychologists. Some maintain that it is the result of physiological activity. Others hold that it is dependent upon the activity of certain of the sex hormones – the chemical substances created in the body which affect all aspects of our behaviour. Unfortunately progress in the knowledge of the creation and functioning of hormones has been very slow since they were discovered in the latter years of the last century, and it is still not possible for experts in this field to state definitely that it is a hormone which controls the sex drive.

Personally I agree with both schools. In my view, the overcharging of the seminal vesicles sets up sexual tension resulting in automatic erection and the necessity to empty the vesicles in orgasm to obtain relief from the tension. The fluid stored by the seminal vesicles is produced by glands, which we know are stimulated by the sexual activity of the foreplay stage of lovemaking; and my theory is that the degree of normal activity of these glands, that is, when they are not under the stimulus of actual lovemaking, is brought about by the action of one or more of the sex hormones, perhaps one not yet discovered, on these glands. Thus the normal rate at which the glands fill up the seminal vesicles with the fluid that creates the sexual tension resulting in arousal of sexual desire – the demand for relief in orgasm – is determined by the slow or fast action of the hormone on the glands. A similar process controls the woman's sex drive, though in a different fashion; in my view a hormone stimulates the nervous system of her ovaries, and in turn a subconscious desire to procreate that communicates with her general sexual nervous system and brings about a sexual tension and the demand for release in orgasm.

As we look at the response to orgasm in more detail as our consideration of our response to our sexual self progresses, we shall become more aware of the great range of fluctuation in capacity for erection and the sensations accompanying orgasm each of us is capable of experiencing. For example, in one lovemaking you may experience a strength of erection which lifts the head of the penis right up until it touches your belly; or the pre-orgasm tensions may be so strong that you cannot delay coming off as long as you usually can; or the sensations at coming off are so weak that you are only just aware that you are experiencing them; or you may find over a period that your weekly average of three to four orgasms falls to one or two, though you suffer no frustration of satisfaction. All of us, highly sexed, average-sexed, and low-sexed alike, experience these variations within the range of our sex drive. They spring from a number of causes, some physical, some psychological, over which we have no control.

So the three groups differ from one another in their performance and experience of intercourse. The highly sexed, besides requiring frequent experience of coming off, require also a highly intense orgasmic sensation to achieve relief, or have need of multiple orgasm to be completely satisfied. The highly sexed man, for example, whose normal need requires a morning, a midday, and an evening orgasm, if prevented from obtaining relief, either by intercourse or masturbation, before getting up or in the middle of the day, will find when he embarks on his evening lovemaking that he must have two or three orgasms within an hour before he is completely relieved of the tension built up by his abstinence. The highly sexed woman, on the other hand, while always capable of achieving orgasm whenever and no matter how often she is approached by her husband, *may* find that she obtains the greatest relief from coming off two or three times to her husband's once; or she may have at least two orgasms or more every time she has intercourse with her husband.

Naturally enough, the highly sexed are capable of achieving highly intense orgasms. They are equipped, fortunately, with the requisite sexual physical ability – that is, the ability to have a frequent and strong erection and staying power – to permit them to carry out sexual activity until they are completely satisfied. This is particularly true of the male and his erection. Where the average-sexed man, having come off once, must wait a quarter of an hour or twenty minutes before he can restore full erection and start on a second round of lovemaking, the highly passionate man can have two and sometimes three orgasms with the same erection, though he may wait five or ten minutes after coming off before beginning again the movements that induce orgasm. A very great friend of mine, who is now in his middle fifties, recently told me that he still finds it necessary to make love in this way once or twice a week in order to obtain release from his sexual tension. Fortunately he fell in love with a woman who, though at the beginning not quite so highly passionate as himself, is able to keep up with him. Appreciating his sexual needs, by her own efforts and with his help she developed her sexual capacity until it matched his – a process, so they have told me, which took two years of happy if patient persistence. (I shall be saying something presently about the subject of closing the gap that may exist between the partners' respective sexual capacities.)

Perhaps the chief sexual characteristic that distinguishes the highly passionate woman is her ability to come off quickly. The most rapid of the average-sexed women takes at least a quarter of an hour of careful stimulation to reach the climax, whereas the highly sexed can come off within five minutes unless she controls the stimulation being administered, or, alternatively, has three or four or more orgasms in rapid succession if the partners have planned that the husband shall retard his coming off.

As I have said, both men and women in this category have very intense sensations when they come off, and I think this may have something to do with the discernible difference in their approach to sex and especially to lovemaking, which involves an unqualified acceptance of their own sexuality. It is this wholehearted acceptance of the physical experience of sex that has a direct influence on the development of love as a whole. And the less highly sexed can learn much from them. While the great mass of average-sexed people have a tremendous potential for deriving the ultimate from lovemaking, unless they are sufficiently interested in making themselves technically expert they may only too easily just 'take sex as it comes', allowing the act of intercourse to become a grey kind of experience, like a permanent diet of mashed potatoes, instead of an experience always looked forward to. The sexual palate can become far more easily jaded than the responses of our taste buds to food and drink. We were not put into the world to 'take life as it comes', but to live it according to our talents, by the exercise of which life becomes meaningful. All of us are provided with sexual talents, and if we do not use and develop them, our total experience of life loses, and loses a great deal. We should not, then, look askance at our highly passionate friends, but perhaps envy them their capacity for sexual enjoyment and do our best to emulate it. By doing so we can add a zest to living and a greater depth to loving. Three or four thrusts of the buttocks is an abuse of the sexual talents of all of us, highly sexed, average-sexed, and low-sexed alike.

The average-sexed and the low-sexed possess as great a potential for the richest enjoyment of lovemaking as the highly sexed, because though comparatively their actual sensual experience is not on a level with that of the highly sexed, by the exercise of their sexual talents they can meet fully the demands of their particular sex drive. In other words, if you are average-sexed the intensest sensations of which you are capable, though by no means as intense as the highly sexed's, are fully sufficient to satisfy completely the demands of your average sex drive. If you understand that you can always heighten your sexual responses by taking your sexual body into your confidence, so to speak, shedding inhibitions, and frankly setting out, each time you make love, to seek the highest physical experience, in the way that the highly sexed seem to do naturally, you will discover, in fact, that you have no need to envy him. In sex, as opposed to the broader experience of life, each couple is an island sufficient unto itself, provided each partner is prepared to make use of his or her sexual talents to the fullest advantage. This presupposes that you act with determination to overcome any psychological blocks you may have.

I shall say it again, but I say it now because it is one of the first things you must accept if you are to be entirely successful in your lovemaking: there is nothing that a husband and wife can do with each other sexually that is depraved or perverse so long as they both enjoy it. It is the fear of doing something which, though it provides enjoyment and heightens the ultimate experience, is thought to be not 'quite nice' that puts the brakes on a couple's activities. For example, because for many centuries now human beings have made love lying down either with the man above or the woman above, far too many people, especially women, have got it into their heads that for the man to put his penis into his wife's vagina from behind is depraved and morally wrong, because that is how the majority of animals copulate. Yet, as a variation on the more traditional positions, rear-entry intercourse can provide physical experiences for both partners far more intense and satisfying than are provided by any other position. If it is possible to have intercourse in this position, how can it be depraved? If it gives a man or woman a more satisfying experience of love for each other, how can it possibly be immoral? To think in terms of depravity or immorality in connection with lovemaking is almost solely a Western, Anglo-Saxon trait, a hangover from our Puritan and Victorian ancestors who believed that *all* enjoyment was sinful and that sex in any of its manifestations was disgusting, though essential for reproduction and for keeping men in a good temper. The draping of table legs, as some of our Victorian forebears did because the exposure of *all* legs was regarded as indecent, is not half so fantastic as the concept of sex as sinful, ugly, disgusting, and immoral, when in fact it is the source of a couple's most intense physical experience, which in its turn deepens and enriches love, and all that love stands for. If the Creator had not meant us to enjoy sex He would not have constructed our bodies specifically to derive enjoyment from lovemaking. In my view, it is a sin to regard sex as sinful and a rebuke to the Creator to ignore the talent for sexual enjoyment He has implanted in us.

Before I·close this definition of the sex drive, there are one or two observations I ought to make about its varying intensity and frequency in the individual. In order that you may understand properly what I want to say, one or two definitions are necessary.

Sex drive is now subdivided by sexologists into three components: sexual capacity, sexual performance, and sexual drive. Capacity – that is, what one can do – is determined by the ability of the nervous and muscular systems to respond to sexual stimulation to the point of orgasm and the speed with which one can recover from the effects of coming off and refurbish the sexual system so that orgasm may again be experienced. Performance – that is, what one does – is determined by the strength and intensity with which one wishes to perform. Performance relies on a combination of physical and psychological factors, while drive is very largely psychologically conditioned.

The middle adolescent years, say from sixteen to twenty-two, are the period in which the newly functioning nervous and muscular systems are at their most responsive and their powers of recuperation at their height because of their newness. An idea of the responsiveness and recuperative powers of these systems is given in some case histories quoted by Dr Lester A. Kirkendall, Professor of Family Life at Oregon State College, in an article in *The Encyclopedia of Sexual Behavior*, where he states that a boy, aged twenty-two, who claimed that his sex drive was not urgent and was easily manageable, achieved ten orgasms in an hour by masturbation, while another, also aged twenty-two, reported nine orgasms with one erection in forty-five minutes, and a third, aged twenty, under scientifically controlled conditions, had ten orgasms in half an hour on one occasion and thirteen orgasms in one hour on another. Though obviously sexually 'high performers', the strength of these boys' sex drives was not so great as that of a number of their contemporaries.

Even a highly passionate man at the peak of his physical maturity in his early thirties would, I think, find it extremely difficult to approach these records by relying on intercourse for orgasm. But if we cast our minds back to our middle and late adolescence I believe most of us will reach the conclusion that our performance rate is lower now than it was then; in other words, that we reached our highest performance within a few years of the onset of our ability to have full sexual responses, i.e., puberty. This is true of the vast majority of men, for these early years of sexual awareness are times of the greatest sexual curiosity. Since these years are also, as Dr Kirkendall points out, the period at which in certain respects the nervous system is very responsive to hormonal secretions, 'a man's sexual capacity is at its height'. Because his nervous mechanism responds so easily to stimulation, he achieves erection very easily; and because his penis is placed where it is, readily accessible, and his sexual tensions are concentrated in that spot, he quickly discovers orgasm through masturbation. Since he can achieve orgasm very easily and quickly, and the sensations of orgasm are so pleasurable, it is not surprising if he embarks on a period of discovery through experimentation. It is for all these reasons that sexual performance is at its height during these early years and sexual capacity at its most responsive and recuperative.

The difference in sexual performance between the twenty-year-olds and the thirty-year-olds which we have noted above, applies also to subsequent age groups. In other words, as one grows older sexual performance declines. There are some differences of opinion between sexologists concerning the causes of this decline. Some hold that a gradual waning of sexual capacity, brought about by the deterioration of the sexual nervous and muscular systems – a deterioration common to all the organs of the body as age advances – is responsible. Others maintain that the causes are more psychological in nature than physical.

Whatever the causes, the fact remains that the strength of a man's sexual drive, even though he is otherwise healthy and vigorous for his age, does slacken off as he grows older. The highly sexed group appear to experience this to a far less degree than the other groups, but even they report some diminution in their drive, urge, and performance. Usually this manifests itself in an inability to achieve a second or third orgasm in as short a time as they used to achieve it.

Frequency, however, has little significance to a man's, or a woman's, enjoyment of sex, provided that each time you make love you set out to derive from it the highest experience your sexual equipment will allow you to have. As one grows older, quality takes on an even greater significance, always supposing that one has taken the trouble to develop one's sexual talents when one was younger. The yardstick of a man's personal sexual success is the intensity of his sensations of coming off in response to his own and his wife's stimulation, and his ability to administer to his wife with a complementary technique which will provide her with her

54

maximum orgasmic experience. All sexual techniques concentrate on the ultimate voluptuousness of the orgasm, for the more intense these sensations are, the more complete is physical gratification and the more glowing the mental aftermath, which is the seedbed and forcing frame of love.

5 ORGASM, OR 'COMING'

As sexual arousal and excitement increase, a sensation of tension builds up in the genital area. In the man this tension is concentrated in the penis, in the very top part of the inner thighs, behind the scrotum, and in the groin; in the woman it is more scattered and is felt in the breasts, all the organs of her primary genital area, the groin and the inner thighs down to and including the backs of her knees. The tension is best described as a feeling of fullness which seems to set nerve ends on edge – not painfully, as in the exposed nerve in a tooth, for example, but pleasantly. Yet the sensation is so overwhelming that you know you will have no peace until it is released.

Once the tension has begun, only rarely will it subside without orgasm. Normally it goes on building until the individual is provoked into helping this build-up of tension to its climax, either through lovemaking or, if a partner is not available, through masturbation.

Deliberate stimulation, either by lovemaking or masturbation, speeds up the build-up of tension, and mind and body become increasingly excited. With the intensification of excitement the activity of the various sex glands is also speeded up. At a certain stage in this build-up brain activity begins to decrease and consciousness of the outside world about gradually fades; all thought is concentrated on pushing the tension as high as it will go. Presently, the mind lets go and the body takes over completely. From this moment, which I call the point-of-no-return, nothing that the man or woman can do can prevent the tension from reaching its peak.

A second or two after the point-of-no-return has been reached certain muscles in both the man and the woman come into play.

In the man they are the muscles surrounding the prostate and at the base of the penis inside the body, which also trigger off the muscles that contol the anus.

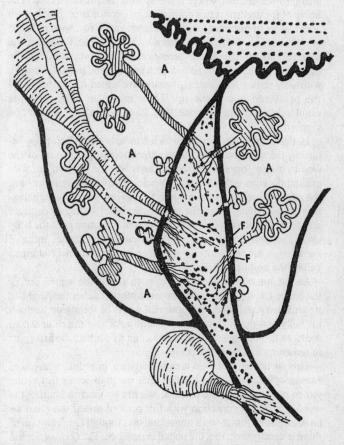

Fig. 9. *Section of the prostate gland encircling the urethra at the base of the bladder, showing how the seminal fluid from the prostate, the seminal vesicles and other glands are ejected into the urethra at ejaculation. Note how the main jet from the seminal vesicles hits the erogenous area of the urethra, so aiding the sensations of orgasm. A, prostate gland; C, urethra; F, erogenous zone of urethra.*

The prostate muscle, which comes into play first, contracts and relaxes and squirts prostatic fluid into the urethra. (See figure 9.) These movements of the prostatic muscles, although they are not felt, cause the seminal vesicles to contract and force seminal fluid also into the urethra, where it mixes with the prostatic fluid. The lining of the urethra at this point is an erogenous zone, that is, very sensitive to stimulation, which increases erotic feeling and builds up the tension. When the seminal and prostatic fluids hit the urethral lining, the erotic sensation is communicated to the muscles in the base of the penis which squeeze and relax the urethra with very strong movements, forcing the semen up the length of the penis and out at the tip. These muscular movements are absolutely involuntary; once they have begun they cannot be stopped.

In the woman the muscles which similarly come into play, behaving the same way, are those surrounding the opening of the womb, those forming the outer layer of the vagina, muscles around the clitoris and the anal muscles. The vaginal muscles have the effect of sucking the penis into the vagina, while the combination of the activity of all the muscles involved – they all contract and relax simultaneously – send ripples of sensation over the belly up to the breasts. Like the man's muscular movements, those of the woman are involuntary, and once begun cannot be stopped before the point of climax.

As the muscles in the man begin to pump the semen out of the penis, the erogenous zone in the urethra reaches the height of its sensitivity and sends out powerful waves of feeling up through his belly and down through his genital area and thighs and then seems to flush all over his body, reaching its peak as the first spurt of semen springs from the penis.

This particular sensation is called orgasm, in ordinary language *coming off*, derived from the fact that the man seems to feel the semen coming along the urethra. We are so used to hearing the word *orgasm* in connection with this peak of sexual sensation we have forgotten that it has a nonsexual use, though the definition of this use exactly describes the sexual experience. The *Oxford English Dictionary* defines it as: violent excitement, rage, paroxysm.

Many attempts have been made to convey the sensations of orgasm. 'Soda water in the veins,' is one way it has been described. A Danish author, Paul Henningsen, has described it as 'Joy and aching – the flights of clouds in blue and green'. Personally I do not believe that there is a man or woman alive who can describe it adequately, for it is absolutely unique. No other physical experience is like it; no other sensation so completely affects the whole body and mind. It is a sensation of the most exquisite physical pleasure, violently explosive, like a firework rocket exploding and shedding a shower of stars, spreading throughout every fibre of the body and setting every nerve on most ecstatic edge. It is the same for the woman as the man, completely enveloping and absorbing both mind and body.

The male may have between four and eight violent muscular spasms during orgasm before most of the semen has spurted out of the penis. The pleasurable sensation subsides with the last spasm and though the heart, which has accelerated considerably, takes some minutes to return to its normal pulse rate, the man becomes aware that the sexual tension has disappeared. For some time afterward he is lapped in a glow of physical and mental well-being. Every part of his body is relaxed, and he has no inclination to move, but to lie where he is, enjoying rare and utter contentment. In this contentment it is very easy for him to fall asleep, and it is this inclination to sleep – which is, in fact, the reaction of complete mental relaxation – that has given rise to the view that sexual intercourse is a physically exhausting experience. On the contrary, sleep is not an essential after lovemaking and orgasm; indeed, only a few minutes' physical rest is all that is required before you can return to your mundane activities, physically and mentally refreshed; though, if it is possible to prolong the period of relaxation, the more satisfying and gratifying the whole episode of lovemaking seems to be.

The woman's experience in orgasm is almost identical with the man's. There is, however, one difference that has a very important bearing on the couple's behaviour after lovemaking. Her post-orgasm glow recedes much more slowly than the man's, just as it takes much longer for her to build up her tension to the point of coming off. She experiences during this time feelings of particular tenderness for her partner, and this is the moment when he should take her in his arms and tell her how much he loves her.

What I have described above refers to the orgasm-reactions of the average-sexed. From some of the things I have said in earlier chapters, you will have gathered that the highly sexed have a more intense experience. For example, the sensations of coming, in both highly sexed men and women, can be so tremendous that they cry out, or moan, or groan, often so loudly that they can be heard in other parts of the house. Some women, as soon as the point-of-no-return is reached, begin to make violent pelvic movements and uncontrolled jerky movements with their arms and legs. At the moment of coming off such a woman may arch her back to such an extent that she lifts her husband as well and supports his violent movements until the peak has passed. Occasionally a woman – though they are few – will bite her husband's shoulders or earlobes and claw at his back with her fingernails. I have even known those who had to wear gloves to protect their husbands from being savagely lacerated. Finally, there are men and women whose orgasms are so strong that they do actually become unconscious for a second or two.

One of the main differences between the highly sexed and average-sexed woman is the speed with which the former can come off. As we know, practically every man, unless he controls his reactions by technique and strength of will, can come off within two or three minutes of having an erection, whereas the great majority of average-sexed women must be stimulated constantly for at least ten minutes or a quarter of an hour before they reach orgasm. Many a highly sexed woman can dispense with foreplay altogether and receive her husband's penis as soon as he has an erection. Not only does her tension build up rapidly but her clitoris is so ideally placed, or is so long, that it makes contact naturally with the penis, the movements of which stimulate her to orgasm within a very short time. If the husband has not come off and carries on his movements after she has, she will most certainly have a second and a third orgasm to his one. I know one woman who regularly has five orgasms to her husband's one.

This ability to have multiple orgasm is present in probably two-thirds of all *averaged-sexed* women, contrary to popular belief. It is, in fact, a natural result of the slow subsidence of the woman's orgasmic sensations. Suppose her husband so stimulates her by foreplay to the threshold of the point-of-no-return that she comes almost as soon as he puts his penis into her. Though her orgasmic sensations recede a little, because it is only a little they can be brought to a new peak if the husband stimulates one of her nipples and caresses another of her available erogenous zones. Or supposing she comes off in response to her husband's foreplay before he puts his penis into her, the sensation of receiving the penis and the movements it makes inside her may, because of the impression

60

these sensations have made on her brain, and *not* because she is capable of vaginal orgasm – which very, very few are – have the same effect of bringing her back to the peak once more, or even twice, if the husband takes some time to come off.

Similarly, most *average-sexed* women are capable of having an enjoyable second or third orgasm if they wait until the sensations have completely subsided and then embark on further episodes of lovemaking. Some even find these subsequent orgasms more satisfying than the first one.

Highly sexed men very often find that they are not completely freed from tension, i.e., sexually satisfied, by one orgasm, an experience frequently shared by average-sexed men. When the tension continues fairly strongly, the highly sexed man's erection often does not subside and after a pause of two or three minutes with the penis still in the vagina, he can comfortably begin his movements and continue them until he achieves a second orgasm. Often he is capable of repeating this so that he can come off three times in, say, twenty minutes or half an hour, so strong are the recuperative powers of his sexual nervous and muscular systems.

It is universally true that after a man has reached orgasm the tip of his penis becomes extremely sensitive and, apart from the fact that he may be completely satisfied, this sensitiveness, which makes renewed stimulation quite painful, predisposes the man to avoid further sexual activity. The sensitiveness wears off after about ten minutes, however, and he can be stimulated to erection again after about twenty minutes. When, however, his first orgasm has not fully satisfied him the sensitivity appears to wear off more rapidly and he can become fully erect again after ten minutes or a quarter of an hour.

Both highly sexed and average-sexed men differ from their female counterparts in that whereas second and third female orgasms may be stronger than the first, subsequent male orgasms are less intense, while the period of direct stimulation to induce orgasm becomes increasingly longer. This may be due to the fact that the seminal vesicles and the prostate gland have not the same recuperative power as the nervous and muscular systems. The volume of fluid secreted by them becomes progressively less if orgasm is repeated without a long enough pause, lessening the impact of the fluids on the erogenous zone of the urethra and consequently the orgasmic sensations. In general, the *shortest* time needed for the direct stimulation of an average-sexed male's second orgasm will be fifteen minutes, while very often thirty minutes of manual or vaginal stimulation, or a combination of both, will be necessary.

Broadly speaking, the greater the degree of physical sensation in orgasm, the greater is the release from tension, the more soothed the nervous system, and the greater the sense of mental satisfaction. It is logical, then, that the object of lovemaking should be to produce the greatest intensity of orgasmic sensation possible. This is what I meant when I said earlier that no man or woman should ever be content to 'take sex as it comes', to believe that 'three or four thrusts with the buttocks' is enough; but that every lovemaking should be deliberately embarked upon so that its results are the best that can be obtained, all things taken into account. But to do this a certain know-how is required; in other words, a couple must know the technique of stimulation, how to bring into play their sexual talents, and it is to this end that I am writing this book.

Many people think, though I am not absolutely convinced of it, that a simultaneous orgasm provides the maximum pleasurable erotic sensations that it is possible for a particular man and woman to achieve. There is a good deal in this idea, admittedly, but on the other hand many husbands testify that they have the most intense sensations if they come off fifteen or thirty seconds *after* their wives. The wives of these husbands report that they also experience their most intense sensations in these conditions; they say that when they first come off the actual explosion may not be of maximum intensity, but that the thrusting movements of the penis prolong the period of sensation, while the spurting of the semen and the sensations of its hot stream hitting the vaginal walls or the cervix intensify the voluptuousness. Why the man should find his delayed orgasm so satisfying stems, I believe, from the sucking of the penis by the contractions of the vaginal and uterine muscles when the wife comes off, which adds a final fillip to the upsurge of orgasmic sensation in the final seconds before coming off.

I have said earlier that any normal healthy man, no matter to which sex classification he belongs, can be sexually aroused, have a strong erection, and achieve orgasm all in the space of two to three minutes. The women in the world, regardless of their classification, who could claim a similar period for the complete process are probably one in a million. Sexual desire is not enough to arouse a woman physically; her sexual nervous system needs far longer encouragement to reach the climax than any man could possibly tolerate.

It is because of this considerable difference in the tempo between the man and the woman that a definite technique of love-play is required to bring them both to a successful conclusion – a technique designed to slow down the speed of the man's rush towards climax at the same time that it stimulates the woman to move faster towards hers.

I have been referring here to the average-sexed, since they represent by far the largest proportion of the human race, and it is for them that I shall subsequently be discussing and suggesting techniques. But before I go on to this, there are one or two observations I should like to make arising out of the sexual classifications.

Ideally, a highly sexed man ought to marry a highly sexed woman, but love does not always take sexual classifications into account, and we sometimes find the highly sexed married to less highly sexed partners. Then certain problems can arise, though all of them can be solved by understanding and forbearance.

Take, for example, the highly sexed woman married to the low-sexed man. She needs to experience orgasm with a frequency which his own need for intercourse cannot provide. There is very little he can do about it unless he is prepared to co-operate with his wife in techniques of stimulation which will bring her to orgasm without his own sexual organs being physically involved; for instance, by oral-genital contact, which I shall be discussing presently. But such techniques can become repugnant to him, and they certainly do not satisfy his wife to the degree that her sexuality demands. In the converse case, of the highly sexed man married to the low-sexed woman, a similar problem arises. A programme of artificial stimulation is not so necessary here, since the woman is capable of accepting the penis in her vagina when she is not physically aroused. Nevertheless, persistent intercourse when it is not wanted inevitably creates all kinds of reactions which can ultimately kill desire altogether.

With regard to these contrasts in sexual desire, I personally do not believe that any problem need arise, provided the partners recognise their incompatibility and appreciate each other's needs, and take an intelligent approach to their differences with a degree of give and take on both sides. The so-called average-sexed woman is capable of much more frequent sexual activity than her classification seems to denote; she can go a very long way towards meeting the needs of a highly sexed husband if she is prepared to overcome an initial natural reluctance and allow herself to be aroused at times when she feels no sex urge at all. More than half this reluctance seems to be psychological in origin, for if subjected to a highly efficient technique of lovemaking the woman can, in fact, be as easily aroused as any man, and the results can leave her equally satisfied. A great deal is made by some experts and specialists of the 'moodiness of women'. While admittedly an extreme reluctance to make love – to the point of refusing to do so – has physical reasons at times, especially at the approach of menstruation, in general this reluctance is the effect of an ingrained psychological attitude inherited from the past. This attitude is really a defence mechanism designed by the Victorian woman's fear of pregnancy, disgust with sex arising out of her total, or almost total, lack of orgasmic experience, and the peculiar idea that if she lets her husband make love to her every time he wants to, she will make herself 'cheap'. While I can feel some sympathy with the first two reasons, the last reason strikes me as unbelievably foolish. By having sexual intercourse, a woman is not selling herself to her husband, not even giving herself, but *sharing* herself, and whoever heard of one partner in a shared experience being 'cheap'? If one is, by extension the other must be, and if both are cheap they won't realise it.

This is not to say that the highly sexed husband must not be prepared to contribute something, too. He should remember that he has a ready means of relieving his sexual tension by masturbation and from time to time he should make use of it, accepting the fact that he must forgo the intense pleasure which accompanies orgasm in intercourse for an experience which is a pale image of the real thing. But if he will look upon masturbation not as a sexual experience but as a physical necessity, he will not find the sacrifice too great, nor will he develop any psychological difficulties.

It is also possible for a medium-sexed husband to adjust himself to a highly sexed wife; and indeed, it is far easier for him to do so. All medium-sexed husbands are capable of arousal at any time and can derive unfailing relief from any lovemaking. If there is reluctance to co-operate at any time, this reluctance also has psychological origins; though exactly what these are and how they have come into being, is not easy to say. My own theory is that men have been conditioned to think of themselves as the sole *active* partner in sex; when they find themselves married to wives who demand more frequent activity than their own sex drive prompts in them, they feel that their role is being usurped and subconsciously resent it. If, however, they are aware of their reluctance they can easily overcome it.

This concludes my main exposition of our sexual natures and sexual equipment; we have now reached the point when we may consider technique.

6 INTERCOURSE

It may seem to you that I am putting the cart before the horse by considering the different positions for coupling – the actual putting of the penis into the vagina. – before we consider foreplay, the mutual caresses of the two partners designed to stimulate both so that the sensations at coming off are as voluptuous as possible. My reason for doing so is that in discussing foreplay I shall have to refer now and again to this or that position, and in order to make clear what I am talking about without having to digress to explain, it seems best to deal with the subject now.

Most of us, I feel sure, when we think of coupling visualise the position known as the face-to-face-man-above, in which the woman lies on her back with her legs apart, the man places himself between her legs with his torso above hers, supporting his weight on his knees and elbows. This is the most common position used by the English, the Americans, and northern Europeans; because of this all too many of us have the idea that it is the only position that should – or indeed, can – be used. Since the human body has had to modify itself over the centuries in order to couple in this position at all, it has come to be regarded as the 'natural' position for human beings. This concept, especially among women, has had the effect of setting up a prejudice against using any other position.

This is unfortunate, for what must be most strenuously resisted in every aspect of your love life is boredom, and nothing gives rise to boredom so quickly as the constant use of the same routine in lovemaking. A girl I once knew was unfaithful to her husband simply because he used the same technique of stimulation and the same position for coupling every time they made love. Though she loved her husband and never failed to come off, the monotony of his lovemaking so got on her nerves that the time came when she

66

felt she wanted to scream every time he approached her. One evening at a party a handsome and experienced young bachelor made a pass at her, and when he suggested they go back to his apartment, she went, knowing quite well how it would finish. His technique was so different from her husband's and the experience of lovemaking he gave her so ecstatic she became infatuated with him.

Fortunately, she came to her senses in a short time and broke off the association, but what the friend had given her made her reaction to her husband even more difficult. At her wits' end to save her marriage, she sought expert advice, and as a result of this advice, persuaded her husband to see a marriage counsellor, too. The latter quickly discovered that it had never occurred to the husband that there might be more than one position for coupling and that this monotonous technique of stimulating his wife could have an undesirable effect on her. As he understood it, his responsibility towards his wife in their love life was to see that she always came off. He had discovered a series of caresses which never failed to produce this effect, and having discovered this satisfactory formula, he saw no reason to change it. Once persuaded to try out new techniques and vary them from lovemaking to lovemaking, he discovered that sex took on a new meaning for both and as a result their love flowered as never before.

In spite of coming off, what this wife, who was fairly highly sexed, needed was a greater degree of stimulation to fully relieve her tension. Actually she needed multiple orgasm to achieve full relief. Had she not been so highly sexed, she might have accepted the monotonous character of her husband's lovemaking and eventually become so bored as not to care whether he made love to her or not. As things turned out, her brief affair was a disguised blessing.

An indication that the face-to-face-man-above position was not always regarded as the 'natural' one by everybody in the Western World is the fact that it was used as a variation, and very infrequently so, by the ancient Greeks and Romans, and is still so used by many Oriental peoples. For them, the most often adopted position was the wife-astride, in which the man lies on his back and the wife either kneels with a leg on either side of his flanks over his pubic area, or squats on her haunches above his pubic area, lowering herself on to his erect penis. In all the many erotic wall paintings at Pompeii and elsewhere, there is no representation of the face-to-face-man-above position, and I have yet to see a Greek vase depicting it. This is also true of the many thousands of Indian erotic temple carvings and while it does occur in the famous Japanese erotic art, it is depicted only rarely in comparison with other positions.

When I was a young student at the Sorbonne, there was passed among us an illustrated book called *The Thirty-two Positions of Love*. The Hindus also have a sexual-religious handbook which describes between three and four dozen 'attitudes of love'; and in many parts of the Far East it has been the custom for centuries to provide the newly-wed couple with a roll of pictures showing a score of ways in which to couple – in Japan they are known as *pillow books*, because they were kept under the pillow for ready consultation. Many of the more exotic positions, however, require such a contortion of limbs that only the very young and supple or the advanced student of Yoga, or the double-jointed, could possibly use them effectively. There are, nevertheless, a dozen or so which any man and woman of reasonable build and suppleness can use with the most satisfactory results.

In order to know what results can be achieved from such and such a position, one has to be fully informed of what happens to the penis in its physical relationship with the vagina and other female sex organs, and the degree of freedom a position provides for the mouth and the hands to continue to work their magic after the partners have coupled.

The face-to-face-man-above position is probably most popular in our culture where coupling – the insertion of the penis in the vagina – denotes the final phase in intercourse. There are some cultures where coupling is used as a part of the technique of foreplay, to gradually heighten sensations without the immediate purpose of coming off. But, for the husband who brings himself and his wife practically to the verge of the point-of-no-return before he enters her it is essential that the position he adopts should be easily assumed. If it is not, there is always the possibility that he may come off before he has made a proper connection with his wife and that she may be 'put back' by the too long pause in stimulation. For example, if he chooses a position in which some bodily adjustments have to be made before both partners are absolutely comfortable, adjustments which entail either handling the penis or putting it in and withdrawing it once or twice before it is properly in position in the vagina, the handling or the friction caused by the movements in the vagina would almost certainly bring him off, while his wife would still have some way to go.

From a psychological viewpoint this position has a good deal to recommend it. For example, it allows the two partners to look at one another and the sight of the other's enjoyment has a definitely heightening effect on one's own voluptuous sensations, provided, of course, that the lovemaking is not being carried out in the dark.

There are, however, physical advantages, too. The 'deep kiss', in which the tongue explores the partner's mouth, or the lower lip, or tongue, or is sucked by the other partner, has a very stimulating effect on the wife and can increase the intensity of your mutual sensations at coming off. In this position such kisses are almost automatic, while the erogenous zones of the throat and shoulders and behind the ears can also be easily stimulated by the tongue. Or again, by shifting his weight onto one elbow, the husband can free one hand to stimulate one or the other of his wife's nipples. Most men, unless they are very much taller than their wives, can generally reach a nipple with the mouth by arching their backs, though in doing this penis-vagina contact may become lessened, even to the point where the head of the penis may be just inside the entrance of the vagina.

Yet another advantage of the face-to-face position is the ease with which the husband can control the movements of his penis and thus be able to regulate the timing of his progress towards coming off. On this subject of penis movement, may I offer a tip? You move your penis backward and forward inside your wife by making thrusting and withdrawing movements of your pubic area which automatically bring your buttocks into play. To achieve the greatest effect of sensation at coming and to provide the best effect for your wife, this movement should have the action of a free swinging motion, very like that of a relaxed leg dangling over the edge of a table on which you are sitting and freely swinging backward and forward. Very many men when making these movements tense the muscles in their buttocks; this changes the free swinging into a pushing motion in which each stroke is separate from the preceding and following ones, instead of the whole series being really one circular movement. The tightening of the buttock muscles tightens all the muscles of the pubic area, and this has the effect of deadening the intensity of the orgasm sensations. You should master the technique of this swinging movement because it features a great many of the positions I shall describe. You will always known when you are 'pushing' instead of 'swinging', because you cannot avoid noticing the tightness of the buttock muscles.

Another advantage of the man-above position is that it leaves both the wife's hands absolutely free. She can stroke her husband's spine, she can apply pressure over the erector centre. One of the first things you should do after you are married is to identify this spot by experimenting with the help of your wife. Pressure on it can have a most desirable effect on building up your sexual tension, and the heightening of your orgasm sensations – she can stroke your buttocks, or she can slip her hand between her own and your groin and fondle your scrotum, or she can stimulate both your nipples simultaneously, besides returning your kisses.

One of the main disadvantages of the position is that it does not allow more than half or two-thirds of the penis to go into the vagina, even when the wife is so built as to allow the greatest degree of penetration in this position. In Chapter 3 I made a brief reference to differences in position of the vaginal entrance in individual women. In some it is set well back between the legs, while in others it is set close up under the pelvic bone, in which case the urethral opening and clitoris are very close together. Between these two extremes are other settings, and though between the extremes there may not be more than an inch or an inch and a half, this tiny distance can make all the difference to the length of penis admitted by the vagina.

The reason for this is quite simple when the anatomy of the couple is taken into consideration. As you place yourself above your partner your penis, which will be at its maximum stiffness by the time you are ready for coupling, will be almost parallel with the bed. Because of the position of your penis in relation with the rest of your body in order to enter the vagina that is set far back, its tip will have to be lowered and the shaft will enter the vagina at a downward angle. This angle depression and the meeting of the male and female pelvic bones prevent full penetration.

In this matter of the setting of the vagina entrance a pillow placed under the woman's waist will raise her pubic area, tilt up her vaginal entrance, and make a greater degree of penetration possible. By intelligent experimentation you will be able to discover how thick a pillow is required not only to make the entrance accessible, but to allow the penis to enter at the very smallest angle of depression. You should be able to arrange it, in fact, that the penis goes into the vagina absolutely horizontally. The thing to remember is that the smaller the penis's angle of depression the farther it will go into the vagina.

One very important point must be borne in mind when a pillow or pillows are being used in this way. The woman's head should lie flat on the bed, for if she keeps a pillow there, the combination of her head being raised and the raising of her pubic area in this way will tend to make her back ache.

You will, I am sure, be wondering why I have referred in these terms to depth of penetration when I said in Chapter 2 that the size of the penis has no relation to sexual satisfaction in either partner; and also that only a very few women can be brought off by penis-friction of the vagina alone. My reason for taking it up here is this. Most women as they approach the point-of-no-return and from that point until the sensations of coming off have begun to abate, have a strong desire to be penetrated as deeply as possible. Your wife will strain against you in an undisguised effort to take the penis more and more deeply into her. At the same time, you more often than not will feel a similar need, and may actually tell your wife so in some such terms as 'I want to touch your heart!' or 'Take it all, please take it all!'

In both the cause of this need is almost completely psychological. Whether consciously or subconsciously, your wife will have formed the idea that the deeper the penis goes into her, the more completely your body will become fused with hers, this physical fusion being the symbol of a psychological demand for the entire possession of the loved one. While you, as soon as you have put your penis inside her, experience a psychological urge to reach up into her and penetrate her as deeply as possible.

I am not suggesting that you or your wife will have these reactions every time you make love. The mood of both will contribute to or distract from them. When this need for deepest penetration occurs, it comes at a fairly late stage in the progress towards orgasm, more often than not when you have reached the point-of-no-return and sense that your semen is beginning to flow through your internal passages. Your wife may experience it by feeling the preliminary twitches of your penis muscles. By this time it will be too late for you to adjust to a position that will allow a deeper penetration than you have already achieved, and so, from the first moment of coupling you should take the precaution of seeing that you can achieve the deepest penetration that the position you have adopted allows.

71

In the face-to-face-man-above position this will mean taking those mechanical measures which will raise your partner's pubic area to the height that your experiments have shown to be necessary to allow the deepest penetration when she has *her legs stretched out straight*. I stress *her legs stretched out straight* flat on the bed, because the angle of the vagina can be changed to allow deeper penetration if the wife raises her knees, either until the soles of her feet are flat on the bed, or deeper still if she raises them further so that she can hook her feet over the backs of your knees, or deepest if she lifts them right up to her breasts and puts her feet over your back. If you have already achieved your deepest penetration when her legs are stretched flat on the bed, penetration will be increased still more as she raises her knees. If at the same time that she crosses her legs over your back she firmly presses each of your buttocks with her hands, though the actual depth to which the penis goes may not increase, the sensation is of very deep penetration for both of you. Nevertheless, the deepest that the average penis can go in this position is to about two-thirds of the vagina length.

The second face-to-face position is the converse of this first one, with you lying on your back and your wife lying on you – as you were on her – with her legs on either side of your thighs. You will find it easier to get your penis into the vagina and keep it there, if your wife first takes up a crouching position over you, her legs drawn up and her torso bent over yours. Either you or she puts the penis into her in this position, and she then stretches first one leg down and then the other, and lowers her trunk onto yours.

Though by putting a pillow under your buttocks you can increase the depth of penetration, your penis will never go more than halfway of the vagina length into her. There are, all the same, some advantages; for example, sight, kissing both 'deep' and ordinary, your hands free to caress both her nipples simultaneously and to stroke her accessible erogenous zones – the back, the spine, the buttocks, the outer and inner thighs, and, if your arms are long enough, the very sensitive backs of her knees.

Perhaps the main difference between the two positions is that it requires the wife to make the main movements, and so leaves to her the regulation of her progress to orgasm. This, however, can be a distinct disadvantage in the early days, when you have not yet completely mastered control of your own normally faster rhythm. However, if you do come off before she does, she can go on making the movements until she does reach orgasm, while you can lie beneath her relaxed and enjoying the post-orgasm relief, which you cannot do when you are above her and have to provide the movements.

The chief point to commend this position is that it is ideal for coupling when you are physically weary and yet have a very intense desire to come off, which, strange though it may seem, does often happen. Your weariness will almost certainly prevent you from having a 100 per cent erection, though your penis will be stiff enough to allow you to put it into your wife and for the orgasm-producing nerves to function to climax. Though it reduces penetration considerably you can prevent your penis from slipping out in this position if, when you have put it in, you open your legs and your wife closes hers inside yours, allowing her to grip the penis with her vagina muscles.

The third face-to-face position seems to be very popular with a good many authors of sex manuals, though I personally find its disadvantages far outweigh its alleged main advantage – that it is the least tiring of all the positions. To adopt it you lie on your right side facing your wife, who lies turned to you on her left side. She then raises her lower leg, the one on the bed, and passes it over your lower leg, bending it a little at the knee and pushing her thigh high up between yours. You then pass your upper leg over her lower leg at the same time manoeuvring your penis into line with her vagina entrance. You will nearly always find that no matter how erect the vaginal lips are, your wife will have to open them further and direct the head of your penis towards them. As soon as you feel the special interior warm softness, you thrust your upper leg as far over as it will go, and this will push your penis deeper into your wife. She will then pass her upper leg over your upper leg, bending it so that, if possible, she can take a purchase with the crook of her knee on your hipbone.

Usually by the time these manoeuvres have been performed the man is lying more on his back than on his side, so that it cannot be called a side-by-side position at all; and I feel quite certain that there are many couples who will not be able to couple in this position unless the man is equipped with a really long penis. Personally, I do not think that unless the man is comparatively slim and has a penis of 6½ to 7 inches, he can get more than an inch or so inside his wife. On the other hand, there is one compensating feature which makes it well worth trying if the tip of the penis can

73

get just a little past the vaginal entrance. The nerves of the vaginal entrance are particularly sensitive to the entry and withdrawal of the penis if only the head and none of the shaft penetrates the vagina and is withdrawn and then put back again. In this way sensations are produced in the woman which are quite unlike any others, while the sensations in the nerves of the frenum and penis-tip against the soft formation of the vaginal entrance are extremely pleasurable. The mutual sensations experienced in this position are like no other, except perhaps in the man-above position if you arch your back and hold your pubic area away from your wife's so that only the head of your penis goes in and out of the vaginal entrance. This movement, however, is tiring, whereas the thrust and withdrawal in the side-by-side position produces no physical strain. But there is one word of warning I must give – some of those who occasionally use the side-by-side position especially to experience these sensations very often find that the experience has been spoiled for them because there can be such a lavish flow of lubricating fluid from both partners under this particular stimulation that the penis loses contact with the vagina at the very moment the man comes off, with diminished climax for both.

More than usually deep penetration is possible in another of the face-to-face positions. For this the woman lies across the bed, her head supported by a pillow, her buttocks on the edge of the bed, and her legs bent with her feet parallel with the floor. The man places himself between her spread legs and lowers himself until he can put his penis into her. He will have to bend his trunk over her, but only sufficiently to bring the penis within striking distance of the vagina, and he should support himself on his hands with his arms stretched out, or, if they are long, as little bent as possible to allow the angle of his body to provide penis-vagina contact. To obtain the deepest penetration in this position, it is absolutely essential that the woman should keep her feet firmly on the floor throughout coupling, for as soon as she raises her feet or stretches out her legs, the vaginal angle changes and penetration automatically becomes shallower. The higher the bed from the ground, the easier the man can make contact with the woman and the deeper the penetration. The most effective contact is made if the bed is so high that the two pubic areas are on the same level.

Some modern beds are so low that they allow another face-to-face position which was a favourite one among the ancient Romans, whose sleeping couches also tended to be low. Here again the woman lies across the bed, her buttocks on its edge and the man kneels between her legs. If his pubic area is below her he must kneel on something – pillows or a footstool, or whatever is convenient and of the right height – to bring it on a level with hers. Having got as close to the bed as he can he places his hands under her thighs and draws her vagina on to his penis. She then raises her legs until they rest on his hips, and if possible crosses her ankles behind his back. He supports her thighs with his hand throughout the coupling. Though this means that he cannot use his hands or mouth to stimulate her, there are compensating contacts, for in this position the clitoris is most often brought into direct touch with the penis and is stimulated by the man's thrusting movements.

In all these positions with the woman having her legs over the edge of the bed the penis must enter the vagina at an angle of ninety degrees to the man's body, which in most cases will mean that it will have to be pushed down from its more vertical erection position. This will have the effect that once inside the vagina its constant efforts to assume its more upright posture will press it – and the stronger the erection the more firmly will this pressure be exerted – against the roof of the vagina and increase the friction there. Since the nerves in the frenum and penis-tip only lightly touch the floor of the vagina, the man will need a longer period of stimulation than if the underside of his penis pressed against the floor of the vagina. This is a distinct advantage for it gives the man a better chance of keeping pace with his wife's slower rhythm. Many who use this position say that they come off together more often when coupling like this than in any other position.

One final point about this. If, when you kneel between your wife's thighs, your pubic area is higher than hers, you must raise hers with a pillow or cushions until it is on a level with yours.

Another variation of this position, gives almost, though not quite, the same penetration. The woman lies lengthways on the bed – i.e., from head to foot – and the man kneels between her legs, squatting backwards on his heels. Again supporting the woman's buttocks with his hands, he works his way forward until his knees are right under them and her vagina entrance is above his penis. He then lowers her vagina over his penis. In this position the woman must make the movements, which should not be so great that the penis, once in, leaves the vagina.

As a variation on this, and depending on the suppleness of the woman's legs, she can raise one leg at a time, so that eventually her heels rest on her husband's shoulders. Or she may only so raise one leg; or during the coupling, alternate them. Whichever she does, she increases penetration thereby. This posture can be taken up when the woman lies across the bed and the man kneels on the floor.

None of these postures is 100 per cent successful when the vaginal entrance is set forward. If, however, it is set back, they are really ideal.

Without doubt the greatest sensations of deep penetration, and actual deep penetration, are provided by this next position, which was most popular among the ancient Greeks and Romans and is still extremely popular among our Latin cousins. It is called the wife-astride position, and besides making really deep penetration possible – even the average-length penis will touch back areas of the vagina it has never been able to reach before – as we shall see, has several other advantages as well.

For this position, you lie on your back with your legs together, and your wife squats over your pubic area with her knees drawn up to her breasts. You will lift up your penis until it is pointing straight upward at an angle of ninety degrees to your body. With it in this position, your wife will move herself over it so that it can go into her with the angle of the penis maintained at right angles with your body. She then lowers herself, with your penis inside her, until she is sitting firmly on your upper hips, the lower part of her pubic area resting on your lower belly. Actual penetration is now the deepest that can be achieved, because the posture of the wife greatly shortens the vaginal passage, and is equalled only in one other, which I shall be describing presently.

You will recall that when I was referring to the sensitivity of the vagina I said that the very far end of the vagina which cannot normally be reached by an average-length penis, or even by some of above-average length, can produce very erotic sensations, but appears to be capable of doing so only if it is stretched. In this position penetration is so deep that this type of stretching does take place.

To be able to experience these sensations, the wife must sit upright. If she bends her body forward more than twenty or thirty degrees the sensations almost cease, but return as soon as she sits upright again. By brief, very simple experiments, she will quickly discover that if she remains upright and encourages the sensations, within seconds they will develop into such an exquisite experience that she will catch her breath and cry out with pleasure. If the sensations become too much to bear, all she has to do to obtain relief is lean forward until they abate. When the intensity has retreated, if she returns to the upright position, the sensations return; and each time the process is repeated the more the intensity increases, so that without making any movement other than leaning forward and sitting back she can bring herself off.

If at the same time, you are stimulating one of her nipples with one hand, and her clitoris with a finger or knuckle of the other, the different quality of the sensations these organs produce combined with the vaginal sensations bring about the most intense orgasm a woman can experience. Even those with a medium sex urge can be so overcome that they may lose consciousness for a couple of seconds.

Though you do not have the same sensations as your wife experiences, those you do have are as distinctive as the sensations of coming off. These are derived from the stretching of the skin covering the shaft of the penis, which takes place automatically when your wife sits firmly on your upper thighs with your penis inside her. This stretching of the skin of the shaft pulls on the nerve-packed frenum and sets up in these nerves and in the equally sensitive fellows in the penis-tip, sensations which never occur when these particular nerves are stimulated in any other way. The sensations begin as soon as the stretching is applied and build up; this build-up, during which you respond with exquisite ripples of excitement which permeate your belly, your penis and scrotal area, your thighs and especially right up in the crotch and the anal area, is slower than the rate of increase in sexual tension under any other form of stimulation. In particularly sensitive men, this already more diffused area of response is further enlarged at a certain point of build-up by the sensations jumping from the belly to the nipples.

As I think I have pointed out, though there is a direct connection in the woman between the nerves of the breasts and nipples and her primary sexual nervous system, such a connection is held to be absent in men. The more extended my experience becomes the more doubts I have about this alleged lack of connection in men. I think, perhaps, that in the majority, the male sexual nervous system may have become so modified during our evolution that the connection between the nipples and the general sexual nervous system has become so tenuous that it appears not to exist. If, however, a special attempt is made to develop the sensitivity of the nipples the connection is re-established. I can state quite categorically from personal experience, and from many of my correspondents, that some men can bring themselves at least to the verge of coming off by the stimulation of the nipples alone. Be this as it may, if you are nipple-sensitive the special sensations I am describing can be extended to practically the whole of your body if in using the above-described position, your wife, without bending forward, will caress your nipples with her fingers.

Here, I should refer once more to one of the main differences between your response to sexual stimulation and your wife's. Whereas her sensations are felt in almost every part of her body no matter where direct stimulation is applied, your response is concentrated in your penis and scrotal area and the immediately surrounding areas, except when you are actually coming off, and then every part of you is set tingling. Though, as I have said, the sensations caused by stretching the frenum in this particular coupling position are unique, they cover an area almost as extensive as your orgasm area. Since the build-up is slower than the progress-to-orgasm build-up, you will realise how specially attractive the possibility of this extended experience is.

Nor is this all. to Added the slow build-up is the ability to prolong the sensation period. Let me explain in a little more detail. If you both take up this position and the wife remains motionless, the constant steady pressure on the frenum will eventually bring you off, while the lengthwise stretching of her shortened vagina will bring your wife off *without either of you having to make any movement*. However, as I have already described, if your wife wants to prolong the sensations, all she has to do is to lean her body forward, because in so doing she decreases the depth of penis penetration and her vagina is no longer so fully stretched. When she leans forward like this, she also removes the stretching pressure from your frenum, and your sensations subside as well; but the moment she sits upright again the sensations recommence in both of you, and with each recurrence their intensity will increase.

When you do eventually bring yourselves off in this way, both of you will experience an intensity of orgasm which can be achieved in no other position. Even if your wife does not normally make any sounds after the point-of-no-return is reached beyond heavy breathing, do not be surprised if she gives little moans of pleasure and goes on making such sounds at ever-decreasing intervals as the

78

sensation builds up, until at the moment 'the cloud bursts' – the Japanese description for the explosion of orgasm – she cries out quite loudly. It is more than likely that you, too, will involuntarily react in the same audible fashion.

Because of the intensity of the whole experience, from the moment of penetration to coming off, I do not recommend the frequent use of this position, but suggest that you keep it in reserve for occasions when the degree of sexual tension is more than normally high, or when one or both of you have a special reason for wanting to show the real extent of your love. If you use it too often, you will run the risk of its losing its special qualities.

It is possible that the first time you use this position your wife will experience sensations which she will describe as hurting her, and which may be so strong that she will protest she cannot go on with it. This is most likely to occur if your penis is seven inches or longer, or if her vagina tends to be a little short, or has not been stretched by childbirth. (I don't think a couple should attempt it during at least the first six months of marriage.) You should, however, encourage her to persevere. She should lean forward to reduce penetration depth and then sit back very slowly. As soon as the pressure becomes unbearable she should lean forward again, pause for a moment, and then slowly raise herself upright again, each time going a little further back, until she is at last sitting absolutely upright. In this way the vagina will be stretched slowly and ultimately will be able to take the penis without anything resembling pain.

Some women, usually the less supple, find that the squatting position gives them a stiffness in the calf muscles and a slight ache in the back before they have maintained it for very long. There is, however, a variation which avoids this, because it gives the woman a better balance and allows her to rest some of her weight on her hands if she wants to. She kneels astride you and above your pubic area, and when your penis has been put into her, she sits down so that the backs of her thighs rest on her calves and her buttocks on your upper thighs. She must sit up straight, that is not bend forward, as I described for the squatting position, to get the fullest penetration, which she can reduce as she leans forward. The only disadvantage of this variation is that the stretching is not quite so extensive as in the squatting position, and the sensations for both are not quite so intense, but still out of the ordinary.

All the wife-above positions can be varied by the wife mounting

79

her husband with her back to his face. These 'averted' positions have little special to commend them, except that the vaginal sensations are somewhat different for the wife, the reason being that the penis, which usually goes into the vagina with the ridge of the head upward so that it rubs against the vagina ceiling, now enters so that the ridge is in contact with the floor. The effect of this is noticeable to the wife, but does not impress itself much on the husband. However, their occasional use makes a change.

Another face-to-face position I want to refer to is suitable if your wife's bottom is slim, your stomach muscles are in trim and your penis half to three-quarters of an inch or more above average, though the slimmer you are the less need there is of extra penis length. You sit on a pillow on the floor with your legs stretched out and as wide apart as they will go, your torso slanting back with its weight taken by your arms stretched out behind you, your hands resting on the floor. (Alternatively, your shoulders can rest against a wall.) Your wife gets astride you, you put your penis in her, and she puts one of her hands on each of your shoulders. Together you both draw up your knees, she almost as far as they will go, you about halfway. You then put a hand on each of her shoulders. In this position you rock slowly backward and forward together until you both come off. The penis will have gone little farther than an inch or two inside your wife, so you both get the special sensations when the muscles at the vagina entrance are rubbed, but the top of the shaft of the penis does come into contact with the clitoris in ninety-nine cases out of a hundred, and of course, with the vaginal ridge, which is very satisfactory to the woman. Even if your penis is not sufficiently long to enter the vagina at all, you can both come off very intensely as a result of the penis-friction with ridge and clitoris. Some people try this on the bed, but the floor provides a firmer base and better sense of balance.

There is another face-to-face position on the bed that is worth mentioning though it can only be adopted if the wife has very supple thigh muscles and does not tire easily. She kneels facing you with her legs apart, and you help her to lie back until her head and shoulders are resting on the bed. This has the effect of arching her back and making her pubic area the peak of the hill formed by her body. You place yourself above her, put your penis into her, and lean forward over her. But you must be careful that none of your weight rests on her; it will mostly be taken by your elbows and biceps. Penetration is deeper in this than in all the other face-to-face positions, except the wife-astride. But as I say, it will not do unless the woman can arch herself in this way without discomfort.

It is quite astonishing to discover that it has never occurred to a very large number of husbands and wives that they can couple elsewhere than on a bed. There are, for example, the face-to-face-seated positions. In the most obvious of these the husband sits on a chair with his legs either stretched out before him, or, parted, placed to the back so that his pubic area is pushed forward. The wife then stands astride him, lowers herself on to his penis and when entrance has been made, sits firmly on his legs. Penetration is reasonably deep, but there are other advantages which no other position permits. For instance, all the erotic zones of the wife's back and thighs are within easy reach of his hands; if she leans back with her hands on his shoulders, he can readily stimulate a nipple with his mouth; kissing, both on the lips, on the erotic zones of the throat and shoulders, and deep kissing are possible; he can stimulate her clitoris with a finger more easily than in any other position; while she can reach down and stroke his lower belly, or stimulate his nipples with her fingers, and a hand around behind him can put the necessary pressure on his erector centre.

This position can be reversed, the wife sitting on her husband's lap with her back to him. He can reach around her and stimulate both a nipple and the clitoris simultaneously, while caressing her spine and the erotic zones on her shoulders and the nape of her neck with his tongue. She, on the other hand, can fondle his testicles gently and lightly run the tips of her fingers along that portion of the underside of shaft of his penis which cannot enter the vagina. (Except in the wife-astride positions there is always a portion of the under side of the shaft of the penis exposed, no matter how deep the penetration is, due to the fact that the penis-shaft is always longer on the underside than on the upper side.)

The face-to-face standing position can only be successfully taken *without* adjustments having to be made when husband and wife are more or less the same height. If the wife is shorter than the husband she must stand on something to raise her pubic area to a level with his. Even then, much will depend on the location of the vaginal entrance which ought to be set forward in order for the penis to penetrate to a reasonable depth. This imperfect position, used mainly by unfortunate young lovers who must perform furtive, hasty acts of intercourse, is better than nothing, for it does allow the most intimate contact to be made and this in itself can be emotionally satisfying even though the orgasm sensations may not be very intense.

There is a variation of this position which can be somewhat dangerous. It is called The Tree, and is very popular with many young people in the Orient, from where it has travelled to penetrate our sex-consciousness.

The husband stands with his feet apart to steady himself as much as possible, the wife taking her position in front of him, also with feet apart. The penis is put into the vagina, the wife clasps her hands behind her husband's back and at the same time he clasps his hands under her bottom. At a given signal the wife swings her feet off the ground at the same time that the husband lifts her bottom, and she grips his hips between her thighs, if possible crossing her feet at the small of his back. Moderately deep penetration occurs. However, the hazards of this position scarcely need enumerating!

Another face-to-face position which can be very satisfactory requires the wife to sit on a table, on cushions to bring her pubic area level with yours, or, if the table is a high one, you should stand on something firm so that the tip of your penis is pointed at a spot halfway between the table and her navel. She opens her legs and you put your penis into her, whereupon she puts her legs round your hips and crosses her feet behind you. Both your hands and hers are free to caress the accessible erotic zones. One of the most stimulating caresses in this position is a mutual activity in which your wife, with a hand around each breast, rubs her nipples against yours while you stimulate her clitoris with a finger. Alternatively she strokes your lower belly with one hand and your erector centre with the other, or caresses your spine and buttocks with one hand and fondles your testicles with the other, while you stimulate one of her nipples with one hand and her clitoris with the other.

The position in which the wife lies across the bed with her buttocks over the edge, her feet touching the floor, while you *stand* between her legs, is much more satisfactorily accomplished if she lies on a table. Because your feet are firmly planted on the floor you can stand up straight, though you may have to have your legs wide apart or the knees bent for the penis to enter the vagina. This standing straight allows you to 'swing' the pubic area much more freely when you make the thrusting movements, and additional stimulation is given to both by the scrotum brushing against her crotch as you go forward and withdraw.

82

The last position I want to describe has much in its favour, yet curiously enough, is probably practiced less frequently than any other. It is one of the favourite positions of the French, and is often called the 'French position', though I shall refer to it as the rear-entry position.

Your wife crouches on the bed on her hands and knees with her legs apart, while you kneel behind her and put your penis into her vagina. You can quite easily make the necessary adjustments to compensate for differences in height. In every case penetration is exceptionally deep, and if the vaginal entrance is set back the depth to which the penis goes almost equals that experienced in the wife-astride positions. Though you will not have the pulling sensations of the astride positions, your wife will certainly have the stretching sensations.

There are advantages and disadvantages to this position. Though you may be one of those lucky minority couples who make penis-clitoris contact naturally in most of the other positions, in this one, no matter how low-set or prominent the clitoris may be, there can be no such contact. On the other hand, both your hands will be free, and while you use one hand to fondle a breast the other can be used to stimulate the clitoris. You can also use your lips and tongue to caress the erotic zones of your wife's back.

Clearly, your wife will not be able to caress you anywhere, but this position is unique in providing one source of stimulation naturally and unavoidably. As you make your movements the erotic zone of your lower belly will brush against the sensitive zones of your wife's bottom. When you make the rotary movements with your pelvis which I shall be describing presently, with only light contact between belly and bottom, the contact cannot fail to be more stimulating than when the thrusting movements are vigorous and the bodies make heavy contact, for your pubic hair as well as the hairy skin of your belly will brush against your wife's skin and have the particularly rousing effect on her that light touches of the lips and tongue invariably have. The effect on you will be equally pleasant.

There is another unique feature of this position which adds to its possibilities for stimulation. Owing to the alignment of some of your wife's internal organs – the angle of the vagina, the womb, the rectum, for example – as you move your penis backward and forward inside her, a little air flows in as you draw back and is forced out again as you push your penis forward. If your movements are at all vigorous this air comes out of the vagina with the sound that would be made if you lightly smacked any part of the body with the slightly curved palm of the hand. As sounds play quite a prominent role in the sexual arousal of most people this can add considerably to the heightening of the sexual tension in both of you.

There are a number of variations in the rear-entry position. If, for instance, your wife lies face down with her legs apart, you can lie between them, put your penis into her, and lower your trunk onto her back. As you will have to support at least some of your weight on one elbow, this leaves only one hand free, which I recommend should be used to stimulate the clitoris. The erotic zones of the nape of her neck and shoulders are right under your tongue; by arching your back a little you can bring your lower belly and pubic hair into play; and the parts of your penis-shaft that cannot enter the vagina will more likely than not have the added stimulation of being rubbed lightly by the smooth bed sheets under it. This variation can be adopted whether the vagina entrance is set forward or back. If it is set forward penetration will not be so deep as if it were set back. In neither instance will penetration be so deep as when your wife kneels.

A variation of the rear-entry position can also be used when you are lying on your sides, though this entails some adjustment for an effective contact to be made. Your wife, for example, may have to have a pillow under her hips to raise her pubic area to the height of yours; or her vagina entrance may be set so far forward that for your penis to get even its head inside she will have to draw her knees upward towards her chest and you will have to lie, so to speak, under her. This is not a variation I can honestly recommend because the penis runs the risk of slipping out of the vagina more easily than in any other position.

Quite as effective as the wife-kneeling position is the variation in which she stands and leans forward over a table as far as she can go, with cushions under her for comfort. You stand behind her between her parted legs, put your penis into her and remain standing upright while you make your movements, though you should try to get one hand on her clitoris. She may have to stand on something to raise her pubic area if you are much taller than she is. And a variation on this, though penetration is not so deep and you will not be able to attend to her clitoris or provide her with any other stimulation except your pubic hair against her bottom, is for you to support her legs, which will be stretched out behind her, with your hands.

Now, though your wife may have made no objection at all to having her back to you in the wife-astride or sitting-on-a-chair positions, you may find that you will have to overcome her prejudices against any other rear-entry position. This is yet another thing for which we have to thank our Victorian ancestors. The prejudice, which is purely psychological, springs from the fact that when she assumes a quadruped position to allow you to make a rear-entry you are both adopting the position in which most animals copulate, thus bringing yourselves down to the level of animals, with her role a particularly degrading one. If this prejudice does exist in your wife's mind you will have to use a good deal of tact to break it down. One argument you might use is that the fact that humans are able to adopt any number of positions for coupling, against the animals' one, is yet another mark of Man's sexual superiority over the animal world. The results of rear-entry coupling are extremely well worthwhile, but if your wife continues to object, give up. No wife should be forced to use a position that is truly against her inclination.

Once more I repeat that both of you must accept the fact that in lovemaking between man and wife there is nothing either of you can do – outside definite sadistic or masochistic acts – that is unnatural or perverted.

It is quite extraordinary how many men have the notion that the only movement they can make with the penis inside the vagina is the backward-and-forward in-and-out thrusting and withdrawal. Certainly this movement provides the best stimulation for the man and of course it is pleasant for the woman, and if the penis makes contact with the clitoris, stimulates her, too. On the other hand, it so stimulates the man that it hastens considerably his progress towards coming off, and since he is naturally quicker than the woman this is not always desirable. Just as pleasant sensations are aroused in the woman if instead of thrusting and withdrawing you press your pubic area, not too heavily, on hers and move your hips from side to side. Even if your penis does not rub directly against her clitoris in the backward and forward movements, this pressing of the pubic areas combined with the side-to-side movement of your hips will almost certainly stimulate her clitoral area, if not that part of the clitoris that is exposed. But the main advantage is that while the side-to-side movements will increase her sexual tension they will have very little effect on yours, thus making your build-up of tension much slower, so that you can pace her more easily.

Another movement that is also advantageous from this point of view, though it is slightly more stimulating for you, is a circular movement made by your pubic area. You press on her pubic area with yours, as I described previously, but instead of moving your hips from side to side, you rotate your pubic area. In order to do this you will find that you have to make thrusting movements with the penis. But instead of withdrawing practically the whole length of the penis as you do in your normal backward and forward thrusting, it is only necessary to withdraw one or two inches.

Both the side-by-side and the rotatory movements should be made quite slowly, but deliberately. This also applies to the backward and forward thrusting unless your wife asks you to speed up your movements as she begins to come off, or you are compelled by your needs to speed up when the action becomes involuntary. It is quite difficult to give an idea of the speed, but I suggest that if you count at the speed of seconds, you should withdraw at one and thrust at two, while you should make two side-by-side movements in one, and a complete rotatory movement in two. I know of one man who, as soon as he got his penis inside his wife, went about his thrusting movements as if his penis were a battering ram, with the result that not only did she never come off and his orgasm was feeble, but he bruised both their pubic areas so badly that they became tender to the slightest touch. By all accounts there are many men who use themselves and their wives in this way.

It is also quite extraordinary how many couples have the notion that the penis should not be put into the vagina until the wife is practically coming off, having been brought to the threshold of orgasm by previous love-play. In a way, this is a natural result of two factors – the determination that the wife should come off at all costs, and the speed with which the man reaches his climax once his penis contacts the vaginal interior, unless he has learned to prolong this period of mental control (about which more later).

On the contrary, you can use the penis in the vagina as a variation of your other forms of love-play. First you rouse your wife by stimulating her nipples and clitoris just sufficiently to give her an erection of the vaginal opening, while she does not stimulate you in any way at all. As soon as her vaginal entrance is open wide enough for you to put your penis in without causing her discomfort, you do so. Then instead of making the thrusting movements, you use a combination of the side-to-side and rotatory movements I have just described, simultaneously stimulating any other of her erotic zones that are accessible. You can even apply finger stimulation to her clitoris by putting a hand between your pubic areas, though you may not be able to keep it up for very long, because a certain slight contortion of the hand is necessary and this causes it to ache.

I have already briefly referred to the difference the penis makes to the sensations of the woman if a position is used in which the rim of the penis, instead of rubbing against the roof of the vagina as it does in the face-to-face positions, rubs instead against the floor. Since the face-to-face positions are more often used in our culture, the roof of the vagina becomes accustomed, after some months of intercourse in the face-to-face positions, to the sensations produced by the rim. However, there is still the possibility of providing the wife with different penis-vagina sensations in the face-to-face-man-above position by moving the pressure of the penis more onto one or other of the vaginal walls. To do this, you take up your usual position between your wife's legs, and when you have put your penis into her, you move one leg over to the outside of hers, and she grasps the leg which remains inside tightly between both of hers. If you put your right leg outside her left leg, this pulls your penis over to the right, pressing it tightly against the vaginal wall on that side; while if you put your left leg over her right the opposite wall will come under pressure. In addition to pressing the penis against one of the vaginal walls, the penis is pulled 'out of straight' and lies across the vagina, so that while three-quarters of the shaft is exerting pressure on one vaginal wall, the head of the penis nudges gently into the rear section of the opposite wall. The combined effect of these two sensations is to produce one which is quite unlike any other induced by the penis in other positions.

In proportion to the degree of control a man has achieved over his approach to coming off, the longer he can prolong the penis-in-the-vagina period before orgasm is reached. Even with only a moderate degree of control it should be possible for you to stay inside your wife between twenty minutes and half an hour. Men who are in almost full control – only rarely is it possible for full control to be achieved – can prolong this period to an hour or an hour and a half. There is, however, one important point to remember. The wife should do *nothing at all* to stimulate you until she is herself well on the way to the point-of-no-return. As soon as she begins some form of stimulation on you, you should abandon your control and go along with her.

If you have a good degree of control, one recommended form of penis-stimulation of your wife can be carried out in the face-to-face-man-above position. As I have said earlier, the inner lips of the vagina come next after the clitoris in their stimulation potential. When you have placed yourself between your wife's legs, you put only the head of your penis into her – which you do either by arching your back or lying rather lower down her than when you want to go right in (though I recommend the former) – and make very short thrusting movements. This has the effect of rubbing the rim of the penis against the highly sensitive vaginal rim. The only snag is that the softness of the vaginal ring can have a devastating effect on the nerves of the frenum and penis-tip. In fact, you can bring yourself off more quickly by this means of stimulation than by any other. But if you have a high degree of control, it is more likely than not that you can bring your wife off just by doing this alone. In any case it will so increase your sexual tension, that even if you can only keep it up a short time, the subsequent orgasms will be very intense.

Yet another way in which you can increase your wife's pleasurable sensations without advancing your own pace of arousal is by 'twitching' your penis after you have put it in the vagina. The muscles used are those around the base of the penis inside the body, which *involuntarily* contract and relax as you come off and by so doing squirt the semen out of the penis. In order to contract and relax these muscles *voluntarily* you will have to practice on them a bit. You can cause the contractions if you try, so to speak, to lift the testicles up towards the body by the use of these muscles alone. (You cannot actually lift the testicles upward; it will only feel like it.) At first you will find their response weak, but if you practice using these muscles for a minute or two daily, at the end of two or three weeks you will find that they will move strongly; after several months they will react voluntarily as strongly as they do when they make their involuntary movements during orgasm. Fortunately you can carry out these exercises when the penis is not erect.

When you have exercised them to maximum strength, you will find that if you stand upright while you have an erection and move the muscles, this movement will make the head of the penis jerk backward towards your belly in an arc of between half an inch to an inch. The same jerking of the penis occurs if you put it into the vagina, and lying still, twitch the muscles. A series of these jerks can provide your wife with a new and very stimulating sensation.

The woman can develop control of the muscles surrounding the vagina in the same way. When she contracts them they have the effect of gripping the penis. If you make your contractions at the same time that she makes hers, the strength of the sensations is more than doubled.

Before leaving this subject of the timing of the penis-vagina contact, there is one important aspect of the woman's attitude towards orgasm that most men do not seem to appreciate, mainly because of the 'new' teaching that a woman is entitled to experience orgasm and that it is the man's responsibility to see that she has it.

Occasionally your wife, after allowing you to arouse her sexually, feels that she does not want to come off. She is capable of letting you make love to her and of helping to stimulate you, and yet, in the mood she is in, this is sufficient. In fact, orgasm might be distasteful to her. At the same time, however, she will want you to come off so that you can be relieved of your sexual tension.

When she does feel like this, and your marital relationship is what it should be – one of mutual trust in love – she will let you know by saying something like 'Don't wait for me, darling, I don't want to come.' Though there will be something psychologically lacking for you in the experience, you should take her at her word, go into her, and reach your own orgasm as quickly as possible.

Finally, no matter how you stimulate one another, you will *nearly* always couple to bring yourselves off, though on rare occasions, when something has brought your responses to a special high pitch so that it would be foolish to pause even to couple, you may want to bring each other off by simultaneous stimulation. (There is nothing perverted in this, by the way, provided it is resorted to only occasionally.) But since, as I say, you will nearly always couple for orgasm, I would like to conclude this chapter with a few observations about its timing.

I am surprised by the number of authors of sex manuals who preach that the achievement of coming off together – simultaneous orgasm – is the perfection of sensual experience and should be the aim of every couple every time they make love. While admitting that it is a very wonderful experience, it does not necessarily work out this way for all couples.

Many women testify that their orgasm sensations are much more intense if they come off first and their husbands do so about a half a minute to a minute later. They say that though their orgasm has been intense, the final movements the husband makes to bring himself off and the spurting of the semen inside them bring the sensations to a new peak. Some claim that they have a second orgasm though in most cases the intenser sensations are really a continuation of the first. On the other hand, if the orgasm has not been very intense, the tension continues to build up very quickly into a definite second orgasm; and if the husband takes two or three minutes to bring himself off, there may follow a third and even a fourth real orgasm for the wife. Women who have considered themselves low in orgasmic response to stimulation have frequently discovered quite by chance, to their amazement and great delight, that they are capable of having multiple orgasm, the cumulative effect of which is much more intense than the effect of simultaneous orgasm.

My suspicion is that simultaneous orgasm is a fairly infrequent occurrence, and recommendation is not to strive after it, but when it does come about to accept it as an extra gift from Nature.

In my view the best arrangement is for the woman to come off first, and then the man, for these reasons. First, as I have said, after a man has come off the tip of his penis is extremely sensitive, and if he tries to keep his movements going until his wife comes he is sure to experience some physical discomfort. Second, the penis, particularly in average-sexed men, usually begins to lose its erection immediately after the last muscular spasm, so that it soon ceases to be of any use to the woman. Third, by coming after the woman, he gives her the chance of having a multiple orgasm and thus gives her greater release from tension. Fourth, the woman's orgasm sensations and her erection subside very much more slowly than the man's so that she suffers no discomfort at all from the movements of the penis inside her vagina though she may have no second orgasm.

In this chapter I have described more than twenty-five positions and variations for coupling. As experience increases, I am sure that you and your wife will discover others. The couple really in love, who use their lovemaking as an expression of their love, never let up in their determination to keep their physical experience of sex always fresh, no matter how long they have been married. Those who treat sexual intercourse merely as a means of releasing tensions very quickly discover that beyond this it loses all meaning; and when lovemaking loses all meaning, love itself ceases to exist. When this happens the marriage is spiritually at an end. This is a frightening thought, and one that can be kept successfully at bay if in your coupling, as well as in your foreplay, you develop as widely varied a technique as possible.

7 TWO ESSENTIALS FOR SUCCESSFUL LOVEMAKING

If any lovemaking is to be really successful, there are two essential prerequisites: the wife must be absolutely free of all fear of an unwanted pregnancy; the husband must be able to control his progress towards orgasm.

It is the fear of an unwanted pregnancy which deprives far too many women of the joyousness of lovemaking and prevents them from bringing to it the totally relaxed abandon, both physical and mental, that characterises truly satisfying intercourse. A woman who is prey to such fear automatically reduces her chances of achieving an orgasm that will completely relieve her sexual tension, or even of achieving orgasm at all. Fear of pregnancy can bring a woman to the point where she comes to hate the very thought of lovemaking. It is this fear which is the basis of frigidity – the inability to respond during intercourse – in far too many women who have nothing physiologically wrong with them. In extreme cases, a woman may reject all her husband's advances and refuse him the use of her body even to release his own sexual tension. Neither love nor the marriage can prosper and flourish in such a situation.

Fortunately there is an antidote to this fear – a thoroughly reliable method of birth control.

The basis of all methods of birth control is the prevention of the male sperm from entering the womb and eventually fertilising the female egg. There are six main ways in which this can be done.

1. By coitus interruptus.
2. By the Safe Period or Rhythm Method (which is permitted by the Roman Catholic Church because no mechanical device is used).

3. By the man covering his penis with a sheath into which the sperm is ejected and held instead of going into the vagina.

4. By putting into the vagina substances which kill the sperm immediately they come into contact with them, but without harming the woman, i.e., the use of spermicides.

5. By the woman closing off the entrance of the womb so that the sperm cannot enter.

6. By means of the contraceptive pill.

COITUS INTERRUPTUS

In coitus interruptus no mechanical device or spermicide is used either by the man or the woman. It consists solely of the man taking his penis out of the vagina shortly before orgasm and ejaculation occur.

Though it is the oldest form of birth control and has been used for countless centuries, I cannot stress enough that it is *not only the most unreliable method of birth control but is also definitely harmful*. This is not my opinion alone. There is not an expert in this field, either medical or otherwise, who does not strongly condemn the practice.

The risks of pregnancy – and they are very high indeed – lie in the fact that as sexual excitement rises some of the more vigorous sperm may have been able to make their own way to the base of the urethra without the help of the seminal or prostatic fluids. Here they meet the lubricating fluid produced by the Cowper's gland and flow with it out of the penis and into the vagina without the man being at all conscious of it.

Or again, some tiny drops of semen often leave the penis before orgasm begins. This is bound to happen when sexual tension is high because in these conditions the supply of semen is very abundant. These emissions are not felt by the man.

It is the usual practice for the man, after he has withdrawn, to bring himself off by working his penis between his own belly and his wife's pubic area. What he does not realise is that the attraction of the egg for the sperm is so great that if after ejaculation the semen runs down to the vaginal ridge, in no time at all some of the sperm will be racing for the interior of the vagina aided by the wife's secretions from Bartholin's glands.

It is not widely appreciated that the semen does *not* have to be placed high up inside the vagina for conception to take place.

93

There are several cases on record of young women conceiving whose hymens were intact, which means that they had never had a penis inside them. The incidence of such cases, which were fairly rare in the past, are now on the increase as the result of 'heavy petting' among students and other young people.

In 'heavy petting' every sexual contact is made with the exception of putting the penis into the vagina. Young people have discovered that the best substitute for actual coupling is to rub the penis against the clitoris until both come off, the boy's semen being spurted on to the clitoris and between the outer lips. Many married people who use coitus interruptus have discovered the intense orgasm sensations which can be achieved in this way – they are only a little less intense than those experienced in coupling – and practice this form of mutual stimulation. If the woman were using a contraceptive device there would be absolutely nothing against it as an occasional alternative to coupling, but with such a precaution lacking they are literally asking for the wife to become pregnant.

Then again, the husband may, in his excitement, misjudge the speed at which he is coming, and not take his penis from the vagina until after the first spurt of semen has arrived. This is quite easy to do for there are so many factors governing the speed of coming that it is rarely the same on two occasions for the same man.

These are the dangers of coitus interruptus, but the possible harmful effects that can result for the couple make it an even more unsatisfactory method of birth control. There have been some cases where, over an admittedly long period, impairment of the erection mechanism of the penis has occurred. Instances of frigidity in women are directly traceable to this method of birth control.

THE SAFE PERIOD OR RHYTHM METHOD

This method is based on the woman's menstrual cycle. The ripening of the egg and its discharge – called ovulation – usually takes place about halfway between the end of one menstrual period and the beginning of the next. The egg must be fertilised by a sperm within a comparatively short time, otherwise it dies. A woman is, therefore, theoretically fertile only on one day in her menstrual cycle, but since the sperm can live inside the woman up to forty-eight hours, any sperm deposited two days before ovulation can make the woman pregnant, thus making intercourse unsafe for three days, provided one knows the exact moment of ovulation. Since this is not possible to know, to be quite sure (in theory) the two days after ovulation is calculated to have taken place are also considered unsafe, making five days in all. On all the other days of her menstrual cycle a woman is considered safe, though advocates of the Rhythm Method, for extra care, add another day on either side, reckoning her unsafe for seven days in all.

The Safe Period relies for its success entirely on the regularity of the woman's menstrual cycle, and herein lies the unreliability of the method. A large number of factors may influence the onset of menstruation, even a slight common cold, or a change in climate. You can never tell when an irregularity is likely to occur. A woman may have observed her usual cycle for several years, and suddenly, without warning, find she has become irregular for one reason or another. Since she cannot anticipate her irregularity she cannot know when ovulation will take place, or calculate her 'safe' days with certainty even with the charts and gadgets now available to help her.

There is a good deal of evidence to show that this method provides a very small measure of protection against pregnancy, and I would strongly advise my non-Catholic readers not to use it.

DEVICES FOR MEN

The man is limited in his choice of contraceptives to one device which encloses his penis in a sheath, commonly called a condom.

The condom is made of latex which, though exceedingly thin, is at the same time very strong. It is bought rolled in such a way that by placing it over the tip of the *erect* penis it can easily be rolled down the whole of its length. Nowadays condoms are so light that the wearing of one is quite undetectable by either partner, while they are so strong that they provide *almost* 100 per cent reliability.

Their only risk lies in the fact that many husbands and wives, particularly after an intense orgasm, like to remain coupled until all the body sensations have returned to normal. Long before the woman has achieved this, the man's penis will have begun to subside. When this happens either the semen may flow backward down the inside of the condom and into the vagina, or the device may slip off altogether. Both 'accidents' may result in a pregnancy. The only way of preventing this is to withdraw the penis while it is still fully erect, which means that the considerable psychological effect of keeping it in the vagina – as great for the woman as for the man – has to be forgone.

The condom has other disadvantages. The nerves of the vagina and penis interact most effectively when they are in direct contact with one another, and this phenomenon is entirely lost no matter how thin the condom is. Some men also find that while they cannot feel the sheath, the tightness with which it grips the penis also has a deadening effect on the already not very sensitive nerves of the penis-shaft. From one point of view this is probably an advantage, for it helps the man to control his progress to orgasm more easily, but the orgasm, when it does come, is never so intense as when the penis is naked. A similar effect is remarked by many wives, who find the spurting of the hot semen near the neck of the womb extremely exciting. Some claim that this is quite sufficient to produce a second orgasm.

Another disadvantage of the condom is the problem of timing. If you put it on at the beginning of love-play your wife cannot pay your penis many of the attentions designed to heighten your pleasure. In addition, its presence forces itself on the consciousness of both of you and introduces an element of artificiality into lovemaking which ideally should not exist. If, on the other hand, you wait to put it on until the second before you put your penis into your wife, the rhythm of the approach to coming off is broken. Though you may quickly catch up, your wife, while waiting for you to cope with the sheath, may fall so far back in her progress that she will not be able to come off before you do. To some extent this can be avoided if she puts it on while you continue the stimulation of her clitoris, but the touch of her hands at this late moment may be enough to bring you off before you can enter her.

The modification of the condom is popularly known as the Malthus cap or the American tip. It is a kind of miniature sheath, also made of thin latex, designed to fit over the head of the penis only. It is moulded more or less to the shape of the penis-head, closing at its base to a small, reinforced opening which must be stretched to go over the penis-head. This rim is so strong that it holds the device in place even when the penis has completely subsided, thus providing an advantage over the full sheath by allowing the partners to stay coupled after orgasm.

Another advantage is that by leaving the shaft on the penis naked it allows the greater part of the penis to have direct contact with the vagina.

96

On the other hand, it has disadvantages which the full sheath has not. For example, the rim clamps itself if not directly on, then very near the orgasm-producing nerves in the frenum and penis-tip. This deadens their sensitivity and though this delays orgasm when you do come off the feelings are less intense.

The greatest disadvantage of the cap lies in the difficulty of putting it on. Both the condom and the cap must contain as little air as possible when in position so as to accommodate the semen without causing the latex to burst. It is easy to reduce the air in the condom merely by holding the teat at the end tightly between the fingers of one hand as you roll it over the penis with the other. The rim of the *cap*, however, is generally so strong that the fingers of both hands are required to stretch it far enough open to slip over the penis-head.

For the best results you must fit the cap at the beginning of fore-play. But again, like the condom, this will prevent your wife from caressing your penis-head. And if you wait till you are ready to go into your wife you may take such a time in getting the cap into position that she, while waiting, may have fallen so far behind that you have to start love-play all over again.

These are the only two mechanical devices available to the man, and although they provide a high degree of protection against unwanted pregnancy, they are not ideal. What is ideal is a device which, if properly used, assures the maximum degree of protection, can be applied before lovemaking, and need not be removed until some time afterward, and which is also absolutely undetectable by both partners. Fortunately such a device is available for the wife.

SPERMICIDES AND THE CERVICAL AND DUTCH CAPS

Spermicides are sold in the form of pessaries, one of which is pushed high up into the vagina, where body heat causes it to melt and produce a layer of spermicidal foam which is intended to cover the whole entrance to the womb and kill any sperm before they reach its interior.

I say intended because, used on their own, spermicidal pessaries give a low degree of protection against pregnancy. Sometimes they do not melt sufficiently before the sperm are injected into the vagina, usually because they have not been inserted long enough before coupling. Sometimes, because the woman's fingers are not long enough, they are deposited only halfway up the vagina, and though they may act quite properly, the head of the penis pierces the foam and spurts the semen on the cervix side of it, giving the sperm free passage into the womb.

But even if they are inserted properly and melt properly they have one great disadvantage in that their use does not allow the wife to play an active role in lovemaking and reduces the positions for coupling to one. For if the wife does not lie on her back from the moment she has inserted the pessary, it may slip out, unknown to husband and wife, before it has melted; or if it does melt properly and she raises her torso at all, either during love-play, or for coupling, the liquid may trickle out of the vagina and what is left behind may not be sufficient to cope with all the sperm. If the liquid does trickle out it prohibits the husband from caressing his wife's genitals with his lips or tongue, on account of the unpleasant taste of the chemicals and their slightly poisonous effect if taken internally.

Statistics show that if used on their own the proportion of failures is sufficiently high for the pessary not to be recommended as a contraceptive method. On the other hand, they have a very high value as a second line of defence if used in addition to a mechanical device worn by the wife.

The mechanical device for women is a cap that shuts off the entrance to the womb. Caps are of two kinds: the cervical cap, which fits tightly over the neck of the womb; and the diaphragm, or Dutch cap, which shuts off the entrance to the womb by clipping onto the far side of the cervix and tucking tightly in behind the pubic bone at the front end of the vagina.

Both must be fitted by a doctor in the first instance. No two women's measurements are exactly the same, so the cervix must be measured in the one case, and the distance from the cervix to the pubic bone in the other.

As a contraceptive device, the cervical cap, if used with a spermicidal jelly and properly inserted, is 100 per cent reliable. But it has two drawbacks: If it is made of rubber it has to be removed every twenty-four hours. It is not easy to remove, and there is the possibility that the wife may scratch her cervix and vagina while doing so, with the risk of setting up infection. Also, improperly placed, it is quite useless. If, however, it is made of lucite, it can be left in position as long as three weeks without causing irritation or inflammation; but as lucite is a hard material, if in making its thrusts the penis touches it, it can be quite painful for both husband and wife.

This leaves the Dutch cap, and fortunately it is the one contraceptive device which has all the requirements I have listed earlier. It is easy to fit and remove; it is 100 per cent reliable if used with a spermicidal paste; it cannot be felt by the wife or husband

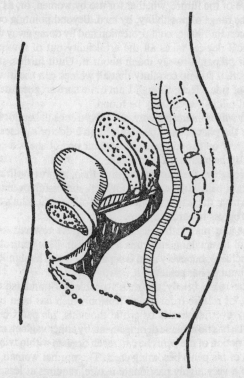

Fig. 10. *When the penis enters the vagina, it pushes the cap up to the rim. The cap cannot be felt by either husband or wife.*

when in place; it allows the penis to go naked into the vagina and the semen to be spurted into the vagina, thus allowing the partners the full benefits of the sensations produced; it can be kept absolutely clean with ease; it cannot cause any damage.

I must stress, however, that the wife must go to her doctor to be measured and provided with a cap her exact size. This is absolutely necessary, for if the cap does not fit perfectly, it is absolutely useless.

THE PILL

Lastly the contraceptive pill, which is undoubtedly the contraceptive of the future, whether for use by women, or, as is now within the range of possibility, by men. Beyond pointing out that it offers certain 100 per cent protection and by doing away with all mechanical devices takes all the artificiality out of lovemaking, I am not prepared to say much about it. Until further study is made, there is still no certainty that all women can use it without the risk of side effects, though I am quite sure an absolutely safe universal pill will eventually be found.

If your wife is interested now, she should consult her doctor or a clinic, as the pill can only be obtained on a doctor's prescription. She can rely on his advice as to whether or not she is a suitable subject for the pills that are available.

A thoroughly reliable contraceptive, then, insures the first of the two things I believe are essential for truly successful lovemaking – freedom from the fear of pregnancy; the other is the man's control of his progress towards orgasm.

Unless the man can master his progress towards orgasm, successful lovemaking still runs a high risk. This control is not easy to achieve, but every man is capable of it and he should never give up until he has achieved it.

Let me recap briefly the man's problem. Stimulated by the demand for release from sexual tension which has been built up either by overfull vessels or erotic thoughts, his penis becomes erect. If he has no organic derangement, by either vaginal, manual, or oral friction of the penis he can reach orgasm within two to five minutes of his penis becoming erect. The normal woman, unless she is of a very highly passionate nature, requires at least fifteen minutes to travel the same distance. Somehow this difference in pace must be removed, and since the woman cannot be conditioned to respond to stimulation so that she comes off within two to five minutes of being aroused, the man must somehow slow down his own reactions, which he can do.

There are, unfortunately, a number of difficulties in establishing this control which arise at the very outset. Reciprocal caresses are essential if lovemaking is not to seem one-sided, while from a purely sensual point of view, you *need* her caresses. Yet it is the giving and receiving of these which you know quite well speeds up your pace towards orgasm, often at the very time when you are wanting to slow it down. The first thing you must learn, therefore, is to recognise how far you can let your sensations mount without coming to the point-of-no-return. Once you have reached this point, your wife must stop caressing you, and you must help your sensations to subside by relaxing all your genital area and taking some really deep breaths. When you no longer feel that you will come off quickly, let your wife start caressing you again, and this process of stop-go can continue until she decides that she is ready for you to go into her and to come off, preceding you by a few seconds. The more often you come to the brink, drop back, and come on again, the more intense your orgasm will be. You, on the other hand, must maintain your steady stimulation of her, otherwise she may not be able to come.

Learning to control your speed towards orgasm takes quite a bit of learning, and it may require several months, perhaps even a couple of years, before you have a very high degree of mastery. You have one thing to help you – the more you submit to your wife's caresses the more the orgasm-producing nerves will become accustomed to them, and by degrees you will find eventually that you will need longer periods of stimulation. This is not to say that the nerves are impaired, merely that they are, so to speak, conditioned.

Control, however, is not entirely reliant on your physical reaction to stimulation. It is possible to enhance your mastery of your progress to orgasm by psychological means. Though I know it will sound odd, especially as you will have to do it at the very time when you think you should be concentrating on lovemaking, nevertheless, the benefits are well worthwhile. It is this: while you are stimulating your wife and being stimulated by her, every now and again distract your concentration from what you are doing and what is being done to you by thinking about something quite divorced from lovemaking. I don't suggest that you go as far as some Indian experts advise and smoke a cigarette while your wife does all the stimulation of you and herself; or as far as some Japanese 'pillow books' suggest and have a maid serve you with tea while your wife does all the work, but you should quite deliberately force your thoughts to something entirely unconnected with sex. Half a minute of such extraneous thoughts while you continue your stimulation of your wife and she stimulates you will have quite an extraordinary deadening effect on nervous responses. Though you will probably remain aware of your growing excitement from her caresses, your responses will appear to be much less acute. Should you reach the point when your wife ought to stop, you will be aware of it, since the sensations at this stage are so intense that they cut through all thoughts. Do not spend longer than half a minute at a time at the psychological braking; repeat whenever you feel the need of it. In this way your sexual rapport with your wife will not be harmed.

Men who have been circumcised have a head start in this matter of learning control, for with the removal of the protective covering of the foreskin, the membrane covering the head of the penis thickens and this automatically lessens the apparent sensitivity of the nerves in the tip. I say 'apparent' sensitivity, for the nerves do *not* lose any of their sensitivity, but merely take longer to stimulate. Once they are stimulated, however, the circumcised man has equally intense sensations as the man whose foreskin is intact.

It is also possible nowadays to call medicine to one's aid. Ointments are now manufactured in which one of the ingredients is 1 per cent of cinchocaine, or nupercaine or pontocaine, chemicals with anesthetic qualities. If one of these is applied liberally to the head of the penis, the foreskin, the shaft, and particularly the frenum about two hours before lovemaking begins, the orgasm-producing nerves are so anesthetised that the speed to orgasm is greatly slowed down. This anesthetic does not affect erection in any way, and the sensations of coming off are normal. If the penis is thoroughly washed before lovemaking, the anesthetic effect of the ointment is unimpaired, and the wife can indulge in mouth-to-penis caresses without any ill effect to herself.

Originally these ointments were invented to help men who suffered from what is known as premature ejaculation; that is, they either come off at the slightest touch, or as soon as the tip of the penis touches the vaginal entrance, or within a few seconds of putting the penis into the vagina, a disability arising from over-sensitive nerves that prevents them from indulging in normal love-making and can lead to a breakdown of the marriage because it leaves the wife *always* totally unrelieved. Doctors who prescribe the use of these ointments report that men suffering from premature ejaculation who use them are able to prolong lovemaking for anything from half an hour to an hour before coming off.

There is no reason why any man, regardless of whether he suffers from real premature ejaculation, should not use such ointments to secure control over his speed towards orgasm and I would recommend them. Application at half the prescribed time should be made before beginning lovemaking, which will have the effect of reducing the action of the anaesthetic by half. This measure, plus your usual procedures for obtaining control over progress to orgasm, will give you success earlier.

The main point to be accepted by you in this matter of controlling your progress towards coming off is that however expert you become, you will still have to sacrifice some of your sexual convenience. Lovemaking involves a number of factors – contact, sight, thought, fantasy, a desire to satisfy the partner, and so on – all of which seem to be deliberately designed to hasten the male's climax rather than delay it. To control the natural speed of your sexual responses to one or a combination of these factors entails a deliberate effort on your part which to a certain extent must detract from your ultimate experience. What you should try to achieve is a technique that successfully delays your responses during the first two-thirds of lovemaking and allows you to go into the final phase with complete physical and mental abandon. You may take it from me that the acquisition of control is not easily come by, though, on the other hand, every man can acquire it if he sets his mind to it and by experiment and application can confine his sacrifice of sexual convenience to the early stages of lovemaking, and at the climax so let himself go that the awareness of the early sacrifice is erased by the ecstasy of the orgasm of both partners.

One final tip. You will find that your achievement of control will come to you more easily if you make love more frequently than your sexual urge demands. You do not *eat* only when you are starving or *sleep* only when you are exhausted. There is no reason why you should wait to make love until your sexual tension has reached such a pitch that it must have relief. If your sex drive demands that you make love three times a week, then make love five times. The experience of the two occasions when you have to be deliberately aroused will help you to a more effective control on the occasions when you are compelled by your sex drive to seek relief.

And a last observation: As you grow older your sex drive gradually loses some of its impetus. In other words, the older you get the less of a tool of your sex drive you become, control comes more easily and then it is a matter of skill and technique to derive the greatest joy and happiness from lovemaking. The perfecting of the art of love is a continuing process which goes on throughout a man's life. I am now in my late fifties, and I have enjoyed physical sex all my life, but I am finding that each time I make love, though the occasions may be fewer, my experience is ineffably richer, despite the fact that throughout nearly thirty-five years of marriage I have always tried to extract from lovemaking the most intense voluptuous sensations I could. Whether my physical sensations are actually as intense as they seem, their effect on me is no less magnificent than were my responses to lovemaking say twenty-five years ago when I was in the prime of my early thirties. Far too many men, fearing a diminution of sexual capacity with advancing age, render themselves sexually incompetent, when, if they would only tell themselves that they will make love to the very last, they could always overcompensate any organic influences to which they are inevitably subject as they grow older. But this, I am sure, is only possible if there has been a deliberate and determined effort throughout married life to develop the technique of lovemaking, a refusal to accept sex merely at its face value.

In this chapter I have been able to give only an indication of what a couple should aim for – the removal of all fear of an unwanted pregnancy; and the supreme necessity for the man to learn control of what may be called his sexual speed. Beyond that, though I have been able to be dogmatic about birth-control methods, with regard to your control of your sexual speed I have been able to give you no more than a few suggestions. I am quite certain that you will find these useful, but you will soon discover that it is your own experimenting that will, in the long run, achieve for you the ideal I am so strongly advocating.

I repeat – you will find that it will require careful thought, great persistence, and infinite patience. It may take you up to a couple of years to acquire such a degree of control that, perhaps ninety-eight times out of a hundred, you will be able to embark on love-making confident that you will successfully dictate to your sexual nervous system what its reaction shall be at any given moment along the path to orgasm. Believe me, every man who has achieved this control will tell you that all the time and effort and thought he put into it has been a hundred times rewarded by the ultimate experience of the climax.

8   THE WELL-MANNERED LOVER
AND THE
TECHNIQUE OF LOVEMAKING

I am now going to assume that you and your partner have adopted
a method of birth control that gives you a maximum protection
against an unwanted pregnancy and leaves the penis naked
throughout – that is, either the Dutch cap plus spermicide, or the
pill – and that you yourself have acquired a reasonable measure of
control over your progress to orgasm. I am also going to take for
granted that you have understood and taken in most of what I have
written in the previous pages about the erogenous zones, the
positions for coupling, and so on. However, before I go on to
describe the technique of putting all this knowledge into practice
there are one or two general points I must deal with specifically,
relating to you and your partner's personal preparations for lovemaking, which, if acted upon, will do much to assure you success.

To begin with, I am quite convinced that you cannot hope to get
the best out of love-play unless both of you are completely naked.
Even the flimsiest nightdress or an open pyjama jacket have a way
of getting caught up in caresses at vital moments. There must be
nothing that even momentarily impedes whatever your desires or
your imagination prompt you to do. Besides, during active love-
play the limbs of one partner are constantly coming into contact
with the limbs of the other, and the brushing of naked flesh on
naked flesh is an added stimulant to whatever other arousing
caress you are giving or receiving. This is particularly true when
you actually couple, for whatever position you adopt the bodies
must touch, and the movement of naked breast against breast,
and thigh against thigh, seems to give to the coupling a naturalness
which is absent if the bodies are covered.

Nor does nakedness for lovemaking apply only to discarding nightclothes. Your wife should remove all jewellery and rings with the exception of her wedding ring. Supposing you wanted to suck the lobe of her ear and there was an earring attached to it, for example, you would quickly discover that your caress would be quite ineffective; while if you attempted to tickle her behind the ear, in the cavity behind the lobe, you would almost certainly acquire a scratched tongue. Many a penis has been painfully scratched by the jewels in an engagement ring, and many a painful attack has been made on a woman's most tender parts by her partner's signet ring.

Cleanliness of the sexual areas is vitally important. There are various glands around the vaginal area, including sweat glands, which have nothing to do with sexual arousal, but which very quickly produce an offensive odour which can completely dampen a man's desire; and similarly the sweat glands and the sebaceous glands of the man, particularly if he is uncircumcised, produce the same results in him.

Both partners, as a matter of general hygienic routine, should wash their sexual parts always before getting into bed and on getting up in the morning, with warm water and soap. The *uncircumcised* man should pull his foreskin right back and pay particular attention to cleaning under the rim. If you make love at any time during the day, you should certainly wash before you begin.

The use of a birth-control device which makes it possible for the semen to be spurted directly into the vagina invariably leads to some of the semen running out of the vagina after lovemaking has finished. This, added to the copious production of the wife's lubricating glands and possibly to melted spermicidal paste or jelly used with the Dutch cap, will make the wife's vaginal area uncomfortably moist and sticky, and she will always want to clean herself before settling down to sleep.

I am constantly being surprised by the number of men who do not realise how their wives would appreciate it if their husbands did this cleansing instead of leaving it to the partner to attend to herself.

These moistures will continue to be exuded from the vagina for some time after the coupling has finished. To prevent the sheets from becoming soiled it is recommended that a pad made of a couple of paper handkerchiefs should be placed between the

106

wife's legs pushed right up and towards the back of the vagina entrance.

Little attentions like this, which mean nothing to a man, mean a great deal to a woman. I am sure that you will be able to find many other small ways, as your technique of lovemaking develops, that will endear you to your partner not only as a skilful lover but as a well-mannered lover.

Indeed, the hallmark of the well-mannered lover is the consideration he shows for his partner throughout their love-relationship. You would think that as lovemaking is being used as the visible, tangible sign of the all-embracing love the couple feel for one another, this would be an invariable aspect of their physical loving, yet it is certainly not so. I think it would shock you if you knew how many women, even today, can still legitimately complain that as soon as the husband is satisfied he gets off his wife and with scarcely a grunted good-night, turns on his side with his back to the partner who has just made his satisfaction possible. There is scarcely anything more important to a woman, I assure you, than to be made to feel that her part in her husband's achievement of satisfaction is appreciated.

Though I realise that any spoken reference to the quality of a lovemaking can be an embarrassment to a man, I do most strongly advocate that you overcome such embarrassment and tell your wife in so many words, 'That was good, darling!' You can even suggest, after a particularly satisfying climax, that no other woman could possibly do this for you, that her ability in lovemaking drains you of every ounce of your manhood. You will find the words yourself, and when you do I am quite sure that you will quickly discover how much spoken appreciation means to a woman, encouraging her to make herself an even more skilful love partner for you.

In lovemaking modesty is a hindrance to really successful orgasm and though you may quickly rid yourself of any inhibitions, your wife may take a much longer time to rid herself of hers. Certainly it must be your constant endeavour to break down her barriers to complete physical and mental abandon at all stages of lovemaking, but if you try to force the pace you will soon find you have a frigid woman on your hands, a woman, that is, who cannot respond to any caress. Though her reluctance to let herself go may cause you some little frustrations, patience on your part will eventually achieve your aim.

One of the great difficulties many couples experience in love-making is the lack of a means of communication. The wife may desperately want to tell her husband that she would like him to do such and such a thing to her, but she does not know what words to use without appearing crude or lustful. But lust, that is, the craving for physical sensation, is as important a component of lovemaking as love, and if she suddenly feels that her sensations of the moment would be enriched if her husband were to stop what he was doing and caress her sexual area with his mouth or substitute his penis for the finger with which he is stimulating her clitoris, she should be encouraged to tell him so in the full knowledge that he will not be shocked.

One of the drawbacks of communication between lovers is the fact that there are no vernacular words for the sexual organs. The 'polite' words – clitoris, vagina, scrotum, testicles, penis, copulate, orgasm – are all such obviously artificial words that there is a general reluctance to use them. I personally feel that it is a great pity that the taboo four-letter Anglo-Saxon words cannot be made 'respectable' once more, and even if they cannot (yet) be used in 'polite' society I see no reason why husbands and wives should not use them to one another.

In addition, there are various euphemisms which can be used that are free of artificiality. I have used some of them in the fore-going pages – *'coming off'* for *orgasm*, *'coupling'* for *copulation*, *intercourse*, *sex act*, *'putting the penis into the wife'* for *intromission*, *and so on* – and here are a few other suggestions. The *clitoris* can become *the spot* ('Am I on the spot?' a husband could ask his wife when he was not quite sure, for one reason or another, whether he was actually caressing the clitoris; or 'You're not quite on the spot,' a wife might say to her husband). The *vagina* can become *inside me (you)* ('Put your finger inside me,' 'Come inside me,' 'Shall I come inside you?' etc.). Personally, I do not find *penis* artificial, and I think it can be used by both partners without embarrassment; but if it cannot, then I suggest the practice used by some young couples of calling the penis by a pet name, though this may seem too whimsical to some. The *scrotum* and *tecticles* present something of a problem but I cannot for the life of me understand why *balls* should not be acceptable.

Anyhow, work out your own vocabulary, but do, please, have a language, for it can be a definite factor in the degree of satisfaction you both attain if you can speak to one another. There are, I know, couples who use a sign language and do not utter a word from the moment they begin to make love until they fall asleep after coming off. I feel that a totally silent lovemaking must be lacking something, for this visible expression of love should possess every sign of joy and happiness that every other aspect of love has. This being so, the joy should be audible, since it will not be visible – at all events if the lovemaking is carried out in a dark room. However, here again you must work out things for yourselves, and you must pay particular heed to the wishes of your wife in this at least until she has lost most of her inhibitions. At the same time, you must take equal care neither to say or do anything that might reveal any startled reaction to some request she might make. I refer to this point because just in the same way that you are sometimes *instinctively* urged to administer a certain caress to your wife, she is as strongly *instinctively* urged to want to have things done to her or to do things to you. Such desires will sometimes become so strong that she will involuntarily cast all (alleged) modesty to the winds, and either demand them outright or attempt them.

To illustrate what I mean, I quote from an Australian correspondent: 'Some years before I married,' he writes, 'I had a relationship with a very fine woman that was extremely satisfying for both of us. On one occasion she completely took the wind out of my sails by asking me to rub my penis against her nipple until I ejaculated my semen over it. I still wonder how I pulled myself together and did what she asked, but I was glad I had the presence of mind to, because she came as soon as she felt the semen touch her, and more powerfully than she had generally come in the normal way. She asked me if I was shocked, and I told her of course I wasn't, though I must say I did recoil a bit. But I was always glad I did as she asked, for it proved to me that if I could do it, I really did love her. She explained later that she had often wanted me to do this but had been afraid to ask, but on this occasion could not help herself. Appreciating the effect it had had on her I subsequently did it to her from time to time without her asking – we always made love again in the normal way after a pause – and I had no adverse reactions. In fact, I achieved quite an intense orgasm myself after two or three times.'

Fortunately this man (instinctively?) responded to what he regarded as his partner's rather out-of-the-ordinary request in such a way that the relationship was enriched. Had he revealed his surprise it is almost certain that from this moment the relationship would have deteriorated.

This demand by my correspondent's partner is far more frequently made than, I believe, is realised; or perhaps I should say that far more women desire this kind of caress than is realised. Nor is this the only, so to speak, off-the-beaten-track desire experienced by women. There are some who quite frequently have an uncontrollable desire to caress the partner's penis between their breasts; others who equally strongly want to kiss or suck the penis. Neither the desire nor the act should cause you the slightest feeling of revulsion, and once submitted to, will not. But if you do experience surprise, do keep your feelings from her and never afterwards make any comment on it, except to express pleasure – which you will have.

You yourself may feel similar off-the-beaten-track desires. You may want to caress her clitoris with your lips or her vaginal entrance with your tongue. When you do have such a desire, do not hesitate to put it into practice, *but at the first sign of disapproval from her, stop at once, no matter how strong the desire may be.* Do not say anything to her then, but choosing your time try to explain to her that there is nothing wrong in it and that mouth-genital caresses by both partners are practiced by the majority of our French and Latin Continental friends as a normal part of their lovemaking, and that according to Kinsey, 64 per cent of American married couples use them.

(Incidentally, if you have any aversion to having your penis sucked it is probably because you are subconsciously opposed to it through knowing that it is a method of stimulation-to-orgasm practiced by homosexuals. Ask yourself if this is the reason, and if your answer is yes, then tell yourself not to be so stupid as to deny yourself the intense pleasure of it – for it is the most voluptuous of all caresses – because when carried out by your wife it has a totally different significance.)

On the other hand, there are certain caresses which some women cannot physically tolerate, while for others they are extremely stimulating. The really well-mannered lover will find out as early as he can whether his partner is affected in this way, and if she is, make a mental note never to attempt such caresses. To give you some idea of the kind of thing to look out for – some women are tremendously aroused if one or both breasts are so tightly squeezed that they are painful, while others can only tolerate the lightest sucking of the nipple or the lightest play with fingers or tongue; some are especially roused by sharp bites of the lobe of the ear, or on the erogenous zone of the shoulders, particularly when they are on the verge of coming off, while others are totally put off by such bites; some women have great pleasure if the anus is caressed by the finger, some even more so if the tip of the finger is inserted in the anus, while other women find touches in that spot actually painful; some women are so sensitive about the vaginal ridge that even quite heavy finger caresses there produce the uncomfortable sensations of tickling, while others find this one of their most responsive erogenous zones; more women than is realised like to take the full weight of their husband's body while coupling, while others feel suffocated if the partner's belly even lightly rests on theirs. Once you have discovered such likes and dislikes, always be guided by them.

The well-mannered lover's consideration for his partner will also extend to her desire for lovemaking. *It is quite wrong to believe that you must always see that your wife comes off every time you make love.* The real wife will never reject her husband's sexual advances, and eight times out of ten she will find after loveplay has been going on for a time that she will want to come. But on the other two occasions she may know that prolonged stimulation will only irritate her, yet feel that if her husband satisfies his own urge she will derive satisfaction through his without experiencing orgasm. I have drawn attention to this before in the chapter on coupling, but it is such an important point that I feel justified in referring to it again here. Even though your wife does not participate fully, there is no reason why you should not attain maximum sensations at coming off. It can be quite a stimulating experience if once she has told you not to wait for her, you go into her at once and bring yourself off by a quick series of penis-vagina movements. The sensations will be different for you than they are when she is highly aroused, for her non-erect vagina will grip your penis much more tightly than when it is erect. You must, however, take great care when you go into her to see that your penis is exceptionally well lubricated. (If your Cowper's glands have not had time to begin secreting at full pressure – indeed, at any other time also – you should lubricate your penis with the natural lubricant that is always available, saliva, which you transfer liberally from mouth to penis with your fingers.)

Or again, the well-mannered lover will never reject his wife's

111

sexual advances. As will have become obvious by now, my main theme in all my consideration of the male-female sex-relationship is that it is an equal partnership. In this partnership, the wife has as much right as you have to initiate lovemaking and to conduct it from beginning to end, if she so wishes, with you playing the passive role. This playing of the passive role goes against all the traditional concepts of the male's role in sex, but if the ideal situation of the equal partnership is to be achieved, you can take it from me, the whole of your marriage relationship will be enriched a hundredfold.

So when your wife approaches you, no matter how you may feel, emotionally or physically, do *not* turn her away. Be content to lie and let sex for once lap around you. Except for those that cause you physical discomfort, accept every caress she administers and do for her just those things she indicates she would like you to do and nothing more.

One small word of specific advice at this point. Unless you have acquired a partner out of the ordinary run, you will find at the beginning that you will have to show her how to caress you so that you derive the greatest benefit from her caresses. For some inexplicable reason, even when she has the best will in the world, the average woman has practically no idea how to set about stimulating her partner sexually. You must show her where your most sensitive nerves are in the frenum and tip of your penis and you must demonstrate to her the kind of caresses which draw the maximum of response from them. You must tell her where else on your body you like to be caressed and how. For instance lie on your back with your limp penis pointing up towards the navel as it would do if it were erect, and show her how, by placing her fingers lightly at the back of your scrotum and running them lightly over your testicles and up the penis to the tip and back again, in thirty seconds she can produce an extremely strong erection. You must tell her that you sometimes would like her to clasp the shaft of your penis and squeeze it quite hard; and you must warn her that she must never, at any time, administer more than the lightest caresses to your testicles.

I advocate that the young married husband should begin this education of his wife after the first month of marriage. I base my advocacy on the fact that she will by that time be developing feelings of inadequacy and will readily accept the tuition, if it is carried out with delicacy, and good taste. Besides this, it provides a natural opportunity to begin establishing between the lovers that frankness which is an essential in all physical-sexual relations. But here again, do not force the pace. Watch her reactions carefully, and make sure you do or say nothing to shock her.

For the well-mannered lover physical lovemaking has two chief aims. First, you should aim to derive for yourself and your partner the greatest gratification obtainable *on that occasion*, in other words, to take part in a reciprocal stimulation that will provide the maximum intensity of voluptuous sensations at coming off commensurate with the strength of your sex drive and nervous responses to it at that particular lovemaking. Second, you should determine to acquire a skill in the technique of stimulation and a range of caresses that will allow you to change the routine of your lovemaking so that neither of you is ever bored.

As in the case of positions for coupling and the variations of them, you will acquire the bulk of your knowledge from your own experiments, and I can do no more than indicate some general points that I believe will help you to make a good start.

First of all, you will have learned your partner's erogenous zones and pointed out yours to her. Then you must discover the best ways of stimulating each other's sensitive spots in order to make them produce the maximum responses.

On this point, it is quite extraordinary how many men and women do not realise that there is more than one stimulating agent – the penis – or even that there are more ways than one of using the penis as a stimulating agent. I suppose the finger does occur as a possibility to the man and the hand to the woman insofar as stimulation of the clitoris and penis is concerned. A great many, however, do not realise what powerful agents the mouth and tongue are, apart from their application in mouth-genital caresses, the possibility of which occurs spontaneously to even fewer people.

Let us consider, briefly, the possible functions of each in turn. For the stimulation of the clitoris you will naturally, I believe, think of the finger, and it will be the finger (or fingers) which you will also chiefly use for the stimulation of the vaginal ridge and the vagina entrance.

In using the finger for stimulation of the clitoris, it will be the tip of it that will be most active. It is essential that you should discover from your partner exactly what kind of movement of the fingertip gives her the greatest pleasure. Most women like a slow, steady movement backward and forward along the shaft of the

113

clitoris to the tip, and then as tension increases a quicker and lighter movement, until, supposing you are going to bring her off with the finger before you put your penis into her, you are in the final stages when you rapidly and lightly brush the tip of the clitoris with the fingertip.

A variation is to use the whole of the underside of the long middle finger, placing its base on the clitoral shaft and the tip on or as near as it will go to the vagina entrance. You then slightly apply stimulation of the whole area by moving the finger with a fairly firm pressure, up and down, maintaining contact all the time in such a way that the tip of the finger at one end of the stroke passes over the shaft of the clitoris, and at the other end goes just inside the vagina.

Another variation of clitoral stimulation is to use the finger and thumb. Put the finger and thumb on either side of the tip of the clitoris just as if you were stimulating both head and shaft of a miniature penis and, pressing firmly though not so firmly as to hurt, draw finger and thumb upward along the clitoris shaft until they meet in the apex of the large lips. Continue pulling upward until the finger and thumb are straining very slightly against the apex, hold for a second, then relax and with the same speed and pressure move the finger and thumb down towards the tip of the clitoris. The effect of the pressure against the apex of the large lips is similar to that produced in the penis if the finger and thumb are placed one on either side of the shaft in erection below the penis-rim and then moved down so that the skin is pulled downward over the shaft to exert pressure on the frenum. In the man, this pressure, if hard enough and maintained long enough, can so stimulate the frenum nerves that orgasm can be produced in a very short time without any other movement. In the case of the clitoris, the head is pulled upward and backward, and though the resulting sensations are not so acute, they are exceptionally stimulating.

In yet another variation of clitoroid stimulation the forefinger and thumb are brought into play. The thumb or finger, whichever is more convenient, is inserted in the vagina as far as it will go, and the tip of the other is placed in the apex of the large lips. Exerting a fairly firm pressure, though care must be taken not to hurt the interior of the vagina, finger and thumb are then drawn together until they meet somewhere on the vaginal ridge, and then parted again, the thumb going back to where it was and the finger to where

114

it was. Again, the rhythm of this stroking should be slow and constant.

Finger and thumb are also used to stimulate the nipple, though sucking with the mouth or licking quickly with the tongue is generally preferable to most women. When finger and thumb are used the nipple should gently be rolled between them. Double the response is obtained if the nipple of one breast is rolled between finger and thumb while the mouth or tongue is simultaneously applied to the nipple of the other.

There are several satisfactory techniques involving tongue, mouth, and nipple. Slightly pout your lips, which should be limp, and gently blow and suck, so that the nipple moves in and out between the stationary lips. Almost close your lips, then move the tip of your tongue lightly up and down over the nipple, round it and backward and forward across it. Or take the whole of the nipple into your mouth, with your tongue pushed down into the back of your bottom teeth, arch your tongue and press it forward beneath the nipple so that the nipple is pushed against it and the roof of the mouth. Using a rhythmical movement, slide the nipple backward and forward across the roof of the mouth. Again, turn your lips inward and take the nipple between them, then roll the jaws from side to side. Or, take the nipple firmly between the teeth, though not so firmly as to cause pain, and either stretch it by pulling your head backward or shake your head from side to side.

Quite a number of women find they are most stimulated if you open your mouth wide, place it over the nipple, and then attempt to draw as much of the breast into your mouth as you can. When you have achieved this you should apply the suction quite strongly for some seconds, then let go, and once again reapply the suction.

Another caress which is very effective brings all the fingers and the thumb of one hand into play. Place the palm of the hand over the nipple and spread out the fingers. Then gradually draw the fingers across the breast so that they all bunch on the nipple. Quite a firm pressure should be used for what may be described as this kneading motion. Repeat with a slow and steady rhythm.

Light strokes of the fingertips in any of the erogenous zones provoke responses, so will a light stroking of anywhere on the body with the palm of the hand. The palm of the hand is especially effective on the thighs and behind the knees. By starting at the back of one knee, bringing the hand upward until it reaches the crotch, then passing over to the other thigh and going down to behind the other knee, you can induce responses which may be so intense that they cause the partner to catch her breath.

The palm of the hand applied in light strokes to the belly and passed over the pubic hair so that it touches but does not depress the hair produces sensations so special that when applied to you, for example, while your penis is limp, they can bring about a very strong erection in seconds. In the woman it is almost as effective as caresses of the nipples in causing clitoral and vaginal erection.

More effective than the fingertips on the erogenous zones of the neck, shoulders, ears, and back is the tip of the tongue. You can cause a high degree of havoc to your wife's sexual-nervous system if you get her to lie face downwards and placing the tip of your tongue on the erogenous zone of one shoulder, run it across to the spine, then down the whole length of the spine and up the spine once more to the erogenous zone of the other shoulder. This should be done with slow, very light strokes of the tongue. You will, I think, be surprised at the effect this tongue-tip caress down the spine can have, if your wife applies it to you.

I have already referred to mouth-genital caresses, but there are one or two further points I ought to mention. Even if there is no aesthetic objection to making such caresses, you or your partner may hesitate to use them because you imagine they may be physically unpleasant on account of taste or smell. If the genital area has been washed well before lovemaking begins there can be no question of smell, while as for taste, *the secretions produced by the penis and vagina are absolutely tasteless*.

Many couples, having decided to use mouth-genital kisses, are often dissuaded from doing so because they cannot visualise what position should be taken when applying them. If you want to caress your partner's clitoris and vagina entrance while she does not apply a caress of any kind to you, you will find it most convenient if she lies on her back with her legs apart and her knees drawn up, and places one on each of your shoulders after you have stretched out below her, with your face over her sexual area.

If you want your wife to caress your penis with her mouth and do not wish to caress her at all while she is doing so, she should take up the same position. This allows her to run the tip of her tongue up the length of the penis-shaft on what is normally its underside, but is now uppermost, since the tip will be pointing towards the navel. The frenum is also very accessible. But if she wants to take the head of the penis into her mouth to suck it, she must lift it up until it is at right-angles to your body. The sensations that this lifting would cause in any case make an added contribution to the sucking.

Supposing, however, both of you wish to apply mouth-genital kisses to each other at the same time, a form of caressing which undoubtedly produces the most intense responses. In order to do this, you will lie on your back with your head about halfway down the bed and your knees drawn up to allow the soles of your feet to rest on the bed. Your wife will then place herself over you with her head towards your feet and her sexual area over your face. She lowers her buttocks until your mouth can touch her vaginal area, and resting her weight on her elbows, she leans forward along your torso, until she can take your penis into her mouth. As I have said, these simultaneous mouth-genital caresses can be quite devastating, so be sure you have prearranged signals to indicate to your partner when you are in danger of going too far.

It does not occur to many couples that the penis can be used as a caressing agent, and is, in fact, extremely effective from the wife's point of view, as I have already briefly pointed out. It can, for example, be used to stroke the clitoris in place of a finger or the tongue. To do this you and your wife either lie on your sides facing one another and one of you, holding the penis, strokes the clitoris with the penis-head, or you place yourself above your wife as for the man-above position. You then raise your buttocks so that the sexual areas are not touching, and again, either you or your wife will stroke the clitoris with the penis. A variation of this is to lower yourself onto your wife until the sexual areas are touching. She will have drawn open the outer lips of the vagina with both hands so that the penis makes direct contact with the vaginal ridge, its tip over the clitoris. You then move your body, and therefore your penis, upward over hers and back again, making sure all the time that the penis and vaginal ridge do not lose contact. I would not advise using the penis as a caressing agent in this way until you have acquired a really high degree of control over your speed-to-orgasm.

The penis can also be used as a stimulating agent after it has been put into the vagina. I have already referred to the twitching which you make it do once you have acquired a voluntary control of the muscles at its base, and I would once again strongly advise you to acquire this ability. There is also the possibility of using it to stimulate the very sensitive nerves of the vaginal entrance, by inserting only the head of the penis and making very short thrusting movements.

Another thing that is not generally realised is that if you move your pubic area from side to side after you have put your penis into the vagina instead of making the thrusting movements, you can just as effectively stimulate your wife as with the thrusting movements *but not stimulate yourself at all.* This is a really valuable piece of knowledge, as I am sure I do not need to stress.

There is no doubt that sounds also have an extremely stimulating effect. Many men and women, even some time before they reach the threshold of the point-of-no-return, experience sensations so intense that they involuntarily make exclamations of appreciation, or give little cries, or whimper, the volume of sound they make increasing as the intensity of the sensations mounts, until they come off to the accompaniment of really loud cries. Very many more men and women, however, do not make any sound at all, except to breathe more noisily and rapidly.

If you are not one of those who react vocally to your mounting sensations, I am quite sure you will be surprised how very easily and naturally it will come to you and your wife if you deliberately introduce it into your lovemaking. What I am even more certain of is the greater surprise you will have when you realise the effect of your exclamations and cries on the heightening of your own sensations. It is as though, by making audible sounds of appreciation, you are releasing inhibitions that seem to have remained in your attitudes to lovemaking and coupling; and I think that this is really what happens. But not only is making sounds self-stimulating, the effect of your sounds on your partner and of hers on you is as effective as making a touch-stimulus. If both of you really let go with a loud cry or exclamation at the first moment of coming off you will add many degrees of intensity to your mutual experience.

Each individual will discover what words or sounds most stimulate him and his partner. The only guide I will give is that the words or sounds should express *your appreciation of what your partner is making you feel*; in other words, admiration for her technique in bringing you off.

To conclude this brief account of the caresses which are an essential ingredient of the well-mannered lover's technique of lovemaking – and which I urge you to expand for yourself by constant experimenting – I must give you one hard and fast rule, perhaps the only hard and fast rule, for this phase of lovemaking.

When you approach your wife initially, nine times out of ten she will not be in a state of erection in those main areas where erection occurs – the clitoris, the outer and inner lips, the vaginal entrance, and the nipples.

Do not attempt to stimulate the clitoris or vaginal area before erection has been induced in those parts by caresses of the erogenous zones and the nipples. The reason for this is that if you try to stimulate the clitoris and vaginal ridge and entrance before the lubricating glands have begun to work, you will certainly cause some discomfort.

I advocate a gradual build-up of sexual tension, and since the stimulation of the nipples fairly quickly induces clitoral erection, I suggest that lovemaking should begin with caresses of the erogenous zones. After a time of this, then pass to the nipples, and as soon as you are sure – by testing now and again – that the lubricating glands are functioning well, you may direct your attentions to the clitoris and vaginal area.

The only time you may start with direct stimulation of the clitoris is when you decide to use mouth-genital caresses right from the very beginning. But as such caresses are likely to be used only infrequently, and by their very nature are extremely rousing, the occasions on which you will begin with tongue-clitoris stimulation will be rare.

Another very important point you must remember is this! *Once you have begun to stimulate the clitoris you must not stop except for a second or two*. A slow, constant, steady rhythm is what the majority of women find most satisfactory in building up tension. Any break of more than a second or two, or a change in the pressure or the rhythm applied is guaranteed to set almost any woman right back to the beginning.

Though I have only been very brief in these descriptions I think I have said enough to justify my advice never to hurry lovemaking – except on rare occasions when the wife does not desire to come off but wishes you to satisfy yourself.

A cardinal rule for the well-mannered lover is always to be prepared! This means that if you are using an anaesthetic cream to help you achieve control of your speed of arousal, apply it every night; and if you are using a condom, always have one handy on your bedside table before you get into bed.

Being prepared applies perhaps even more particularly to the wife. If she is using a cap-type contraceptive she should insert it every night, except during menstruation, whether or not she thinks she is going to be made love to or to make love to you. It is possible for either of you to be sexually aroused during sleep, respond to love-play, and couple until you come off, with only a kind of hazy, half-conscious idea of what is happening until the invariably extremely intense climax has fully awakened both. It is no use saying, 'I can understand this happening in the early days of marriage when the couple are young and ardent, but not among old hands, surely!' I have seen records of three cases of pregnancy resulting from such half-conscious couplings and one of the couples was in the middle thirties and had been married eight years, while another was in the early forties and had been married fourteen years.

Besides this, more often than not you cannot really tell before you have been in bed some time together whether you or your partner is going to want to make love. A chance touch, a sudden thought or feeling of tenderness, is quite enough to set your sexual tension building up. Or one or other may find the tension already mounted when you awake in the morning, and if your wife has got to get out of bed and insert her cap the delay may dull her responses, if her desire does not disappear altogether.

Talking of lovemaking in the mornings brings me to a very important factor in avoiding with sex. Partly because of the lack of opportunity at other times of the day – through the absence of one or both partners from the home, or the presence of a young family needing attention, or just lack of time – the vast majority of couples leave their lovemaking until they go to bed at night. It is a great pity that the organisation of our lives practically forces this on us, because neither partner is really at his or her best after a hard day's work.

But the sex drive does not confine itself to the late hours, and it follows that lovemaking is not solely a nocturnal activity. This being so, I cannot too strongly advocate that if one of the couple wishes to make love at any time during the day, and the circumstances are favourable, the other should respond. We should seize every opportunity to break away from the time-rut into which our organised lives have thrust us. We should make the most of weekends and holidays to show one another that we are loving each other all the time.

You may object that making love before you get up will make you tired before you have even begun your day's work. The widespread idea that coupling and coming off are so exhausting that a period of rest is necessary, and possibly sleep, is quite a fallacious one. A few minutes, five or ten at the most, are quite sufficient, especially as one has been absolutely fresh after a night's sleep.

I have already suggested, too, that the bedroom and the bed are not essential places for lovemaking. Supposing you are sitting in the living room after supper with the children in bed, and you want to make love. Tell your wife. It will not take her more than a moment or two to prepare herself and return to you. By its novelty, the act of undressing one another will be a stimulant, while the setting, the use of cushions on the hearthrug in front of the fire, or of an armchair or settee, and finally coupling in one of the positions for which the bed is not suitable or necessary – one of the sitting positions, or a rear-entry position, or the wife sitting in an armchair with you kneeling between her legs and so on – will make a memorable occasion. If you are encouraged to do this, then under the equal partnership your wife may also initiate such lovemaking, and you, being a well-mannered lover, will co-operate gladly.

Quite a number of couples take baths together, but I doubt whether it occurs to many that making love in the bathtub can be a particularly exciting experience. Again a man-below-wife-astride – more usually with the wife's back turned to her husband – is the most satisfactory position unless the tub is a really large one.

Finally, there are two or three points that concern most well-mannered lovers until experience has been able to provide the answers. The most frequently asked question, when advice on lovemaking is sought, is undoubtedly, How often should one make love? Most lovers fear that if they make love to orgasm every time they have the urge to do so they may do themselves some harm. First let me say that there would have to be some mental instability or some physical defect present to encourage either of you to make love beyond your natural ability to do so, and thereby do yourself some physical harm. There can be no hard and fast guide regarding frequency, though for the average-sexed, taken over a period, three or four times a week is the general average, with the frequency tending to become less as one grows older. The best guide is, make love as frequently as you feel the urge to by those promptings whose beginnings you cannot control. If you are indulging more than is wise – lovemaking can become a habit sometimes – you will soon know. The penis and orgasm-muscles will develop a nagging ache, and a dragging sensation will throb in the small of your back. If these symptoms, or similar ones in your wife, appear, avoid making love for a day or two. But it will be very rare indeed if the normal physically and mentally healthy couple make love to excess.

Another question which frequently crops up is, Is it all right to make love while the wife is menstruating? (the popular term for menstruation). The answer is that there is no medical reason why you should not. The only thing that may prevent it is *your* fastidiousness, which can be overcome and should be overcome if you are a well-mannered lover, for your wife may be one of those women whose desire is so strong during menstruation that they experience their most intense orgasms if made love to them. Naturally lovemaking at this time will preclude genital caresses by you, and any messiness you think may result from putting the penis into the vagina moistened by menstrual blood can be avoided with care.

Many women whose period takes some time to get going find that the moodiness and tension immediately preceding it and during the first two days can be rapidly dispelled by the physical reactions at orgasm. The contractions of the womb and vagina at coming off cause the flow to start earlier than it would naturally do. No physical damage can be caused by this, and with the beginning of the flow all the tensions disappear. This is another reason why the well-mannered lover does not refuse to couple with his wife when she is menstruating.

I once asked a wife what for her constituted the well-mannered lover. She replied: 'Everything my husband does, not only to show he loves me, but makes it absolutely impossible for me ever to think that I am nothing more to him than a prostitute or any other woman. I want to feel, in fact to know, that I am a very special woman to him – his wife.'

If you remember this, and conduct your lovemaking accordingly, I do not think you need ever fear that you are not a well-mannered lover.

9 THE WELL-MANNERED LOVER ON THE WEDDING NIGHT

For the purposes of this chapter, I am assuming that on your wedding night your wife will be a virgin and that you yourself, though you may have experimented with practical sex, are by no means what one might call experienced. If you have indulged in premarital coupling, I assume that it will either have been a solitary encounter with a prostitute or at most only a few such encounters, or that your partner had lost her virginity before you bedded with her. On the other hand, it is more than likely that you have not had a sexual encounter culminating in coupling, and that you are as ignorant of what coupling to orgasm entails as your bride.

Both of you will without doubt approach your wedding night with mixed feelings. One of these for you will almost certainly be a romanticised and highly coloured conception of the superiority of the orgasm achieved through coupling over the sensations you have achieved in the past by relieving the tension yourself. This conception at any other time of your married life would be valid; on your wedding night, however, you are, I am afraid, doomed to disappointment.

In this disappointment, however, you will not be alone. Your bride's ideas of the experience will be as hopeful as yours. But practically everything is conspiring to deprive you both of the sexual consolation you are intended to be for one another and will certainly become.

To begin with, all the excitement of the day, the ceremony and the reception, will have tired you so that you are not physically at your best, either of you. Added to this will be a nervousness that neither of you will be able to satisfy the other sexually. No two people were ever under such a handicap when the occasion demands that they should be as uninhibited as possible.

Tonight, probably more than on any other night of your whole married life, you must be the well-mannered lover. Tonight the delusive superiority which your maleness traditionally imposes on you must assert itself. You must be the initiator, for you will undoubtedly be more knowledgeable of how lovers should behave than your bride. For you the act of sex is simple in its physical expression; it is merely a matter of putting your penis into your bride's vagina, and by moving it backward and forward bringing yourself off, and hoping that she will be as satisfied as you will be. Perhaps you should try some love-play that you have read about in sex manuals; but so far you know it only in theory, and you wonder how it works out in practice.

And among the knowledge you have picked up will be one item which, because you love your bride, will be most responsible for your nervousness. You will have learned from books that barring the entrance to your bride's vagina will be a membrane known as the hymen; and you will have read that your penis will have to break this membrane before it can enter the vagina, and that this breaking will cause her pain and bleeding – the very last thing you want to inflict on her at this first moment of greatest intimacy. No wonder you are nervous.

Your bride will be nervous, too. She will be shrinking from the pain she has been told she will have to endure in order to take your penis into her, and yet, at the same time, to feel your penis in her is her dearest wish, though she may not have expressed this wish to herself in precisely these terms. She will also be nervous because though she may have seen pictures or statues of nude males with limp penises, she does not know what to expect of the penis in erection, how much it will expand in girth or lengthen. Will her vagina be able to accommodate it, both from the point of view of its girth and length? Will it cause her pain, apart from the breaking of the hymen, to let it into her? Above all, will she please you physically? She wants to desperately, and she expects you to give her an experience quite outside her ability to describe, because you love one another as no couple has ever loved and coupling to orgasm is the physical outcome (not yet the expression) of that love.

What advice then should be given to the starry-eyed bride and

124

bridegroom to prepare them for their first sexual encounter? Whatever it is, it must be practical and down to earth.

First, whatever happens you must accept it as a normal experience of husbands and wives on the wedding night. For example, it is more than possible, unless you are more than extraordinarily fortunate, that the first attempt at coupling will be a fiasco. Very probably your nervousness or the terriffic anticipatory sexual excitement built up during the last few days will cause you to come off before you have got even the head of your penis past the vagina entrance; or, just the reverse, the psychological state you are in may make it impossible for you to have an erection at all, so that going into her and completing coupling is out of the question; while it is more than likely that her nervousness and over-eagerness to please will similarly prevent her from becoming physically aroused. Accept these things if they happen, and half your battle will be won. You may regard them as failures, but they are not, I do assure you, and you will only delay your settling down in your sexual life if you insist on regarding them as failures.

What I would like to advise if I were not convinced that I would be advising the humanly impossible, would be that there should be no attempt at coupling until after you have both been refreshed by a good long sound sleep, i.e., until the second day of the honeymoon. I am sure that this would provide a more satisfactory experience, but even so, premature ejaculation, temporary impotence, or inability of the bride to be physically aroused would not automatically be ruled out.

Second, in my estimation the nervousness of both partners springs from two main causes – the fear of failing to please, and the fear that the penis will cause bad pain as it pierces the hymen. Both you and your partner are more than likely to have an exaggerated idea of the degree of pain experienced by the girl by the tearing of the hymen.

In only fairly rare cases is the membrane so tough that a quite violent thrust of the penis is required to break it. In such cases, it can be very painful for the girl, and it may be accompanied by copious bleeding and subsequent soreness which prevents coupling for several days. In the majority of cases, however, if the bridegroom uses care when he attempts to go into his bride – I will try to give a few tips about this in a moment – she should not experience more than a second or two of not very sharp pain, while as for the bleeding, this varies with individuals but is never serious, and the subsequent soreness should have disappeared in forty-eight hours.

But all this fear and its consequences can be removed beforehand. Your bride should go to her doctor ten days or so before the wedding day and, if necessary, ask him to pierce her hymen for her surgically. Many engaged girls are doing this these days and doctors are only too willing to perform this most sensible, very minor, quick and painless operation which is carried out in the doctor's office. She will, of course, have told you that she intends to do this.

(I think I should remark here that if she has not had her hymen surgically pierced, and you find no obstruction when you go into her, this absence of a hymen does not necessarily mean that she is not a virgin. Many activities carried out by girls these days – riding a bicycle, horseback riding, very vigorous exercises, jumping, and so on – can very easily cause the hymen to break while she is still a little girl. So, for heaven's sake, do not harbour any suspicions on account of your discovery. If you are a really well-mannered lover, you will never refer to it.)

Third, forget for the time being your determination to be The Great Lover.

This, I think, is quite as important as not being depressed by the physical failures of both of you which I have just mentioned. There are several reasons that justify giving this advice, which I will try to set out now.

One important point which you must take into consideration, if you are a well-mannered lover, is the fact of your wife's 'modesty'. She will have learned that the majority of men and women in our culture couple in the wife-below position, and any attempt by you to couple in any other position will be bound to affront her modesty. Similarly, do not embark on any advanced form of caresses, such as mouth-genital caresses, penis-nipple or penis-tip-clitoris caresses. Confine your caresses to kissing the erogenous zones of the neck, shoulders, ears, and mouth, to sucking a nipple, and if the very first response is favourable, to gentle finger-stimulation of the clitoris – if you can find it this first night. I would not advise finger-exploration of the vaginal entrance.

You will probably know that the vaginal walls of a woman who has not experienced regular and frequent coupling are very close together even when they are erect, and though they will admit any size of penis while in this condition, they will gradually stretch as

126

she experiences regular coupling. After the first two or three days, when they are discovering the basic facts about each other's sexual characters, most young, healthy couples indulge in sex at least daily for the first three to six months, and a month of this daily coupling is generally necessary before the vagina has stretched as far as possible – before childbirth.

Because of this stretching, it will not be possible for your bride to be fitted with a Dutch cap during the first months of marriage. This means that unless you intend to start a family from the word go, you will have to use a condom. (The well-mannered lover always sees that he has a good supply of them, especially on the honeymoon.) Please be careful how you dispose of used condoms in the presence of your bride. Many young women have been revolted by a glimpse of what from the beginning was not ideal, in the aftermath of lovemaking looks sordid and is sordid. She will get used to them, of course, but at the beginning it is advisable to keep them as much out of sight as possible.

Apart from psychological objections to using any position for coupling other than the man-above, if your bride's hymen has to be broken, this is the best position in which to do it, and for the following reasons. First, the deepest point of penis-penetration possible in this position is about the halfway mark of the vaginal length. Since I advise that during the first three or four couplings only about a third of the penis should be introduced, should you lose control of your thrusting movements and go in as far as you can, you cannot possibly go so deep as to come into contact with the very sensitive rear portion of the vagina. First contact with this part of the vagina unless it is made very, very gradually, can cause the woman to imagine she is being hurt, a reaction which may influence her future psychological approach to coupling.

In addition to being able in this position to control most easily the depth to which you thrust your penis into her, you can also most easily adjust the angle at which your penis will approach the vagina entrance and hymen. In this first coupling, the approach angle of your penis is of the greatest importance in breaking the hymen in such a way as to cause your partner the least discomfort. To achieve this the penis-head must be presented to the hymen head on, and not from a downward angle as it is most likely to do. Later, this will have little significance after the vagina has become stretched and able to take the penis at any angle.

In order that the penis-head may approach the hymen head on, the entrance of the vagina must be raised. If your bride has fairly well-proportioned buttocks this will probably be a natural presentation, though, as we know, more often than not the vagina entrance may require the penis to approach it at a downward angle. You should, I suggest, be able to gauge whether the vagina entrance is set too low down for the head-on approach of the penis while you are stimulating the clitoris with a finger. If you find it is, or if you have any doubts, you can quite easily make sure that the angle is right in one of two ways.

The first way is this. When you have placed yourself above your wife, you can, while supporting the weight of the upper torso on your elbows put your hands under her buttocks and lift them up towards you until you are able to judge that the tip of the penis is aimed straight at the vagina entrance. Personally I am not very favourably disposed towards this method, because it means that you will have to ask your bride to draw back the outer lips and direct your penis to the opening, and at this stage, she may have some reluctance to touch either herself or your penis.

I would rather suggest that you place a pillow under her buttocks, or two if her buttocks are slim and you judge that the vagina entrance is set rather far back. When you have aligned her and yourself in this way, you place yourself above her, and taking your weight on one elbow, you can put your other hand down between the two sexual areas, open the outer lips with a couple of fingers, and direct the tip of the penis to the vagina entrance with another. You will be able to feel the hymen with the tip of the penis, even if you are wearing a condom. Keeping the penis-tip slightly pressed against the hymen, remove your hand, and place your elbow so that it shares your weight.

To begin with, push very, very gently against the hymen, so that it stretches. Sooner or later it will stretch so far that it will almost certainly make your wife wince, or part her lips and begin to breathe heavily, both of which will be detectable by you. At this moment give a hard, sharp thrust with your buttocks, taking care not to thrust the penis too deeply into the vagina. If the penis goes into the vagina, you will know that you have successfully broken the hymen, and it will never trouble you again.

Should the hymen prove to be so tough that it does not tear under this treatment, it would be inconsiderate and even brutal to continue your attempts. Stop and try again next day, after you have tested how tough the hymen is with a couple of well-lubricated

128

fingers. You may find that you will cause far less pain in breaking the hymen with the fingers, but if it will still not respond, surgical attention is necessary.

It is worth taking a great deal of trouble over this breaking of the hymen; clumsily handled, it can sow the seeds of lasting resentment, which may ultimately lead to the break-up of the marriage. But even if you are a little clumsy and cause your wife pain, so long as you show her tenderness and understanding, she will forgive you and all will be well. I repeat, there is really very little reason why the pain should be more than a short, sharpish sensation; and even smaller reason why the intelligent, well-mannered lover should not be able to break the hymen successfully with his penis.

I said earlier that your nervousness and excitement may cause you to have a premature ejaculation as soon as, if not before, the head of the penis meets the vaginal entrance; and this without the handling of the penis I have just described. It is most young bridegrooms' experience that the act of breaking the hymen will bring him off; but should you have been able to do so without reaching orgasm, you will find that it may require only one or two thrusts to bring you to climax. However, if you are so far back that it may take a minute or two's coupling to produce an orgasm, this may be too much for your wife to tolerate since she will almost certainly have some soreness about her vagina entrance. If she gives any sign of discomfort, withdraw from her at once, make your excuses, and go to the bathroom and relieve your tension yourself by masturbation. The cases in which this is necessary are extremely rare, however.

I am sure you will have noticed that I have not said anything about your wife coming off. The bride who has an orgasm at her very first coupling is a very rare bride indeed. Though she may have had her doctor break her hymen, there are too many other factors militating against her completing the coupling satisfactorily – your possible premature ejaculation, her own nervousness, her overeagerness to please you.

Even though you may not come off too quickly, you are bound to do so before she does, and your relief from tension will be so great that you will be disinclined physically and mentally to continue your movements in the hope that she will come off.

In these circumstances, the well-mannered bridegroom will take all the blame for her disappointment. He will tell her that he loves her so much he just could not hold himself back. He may offer to bring her off by clitoral stimulation, but this is not the way she imagined it, and usually she will not have been sufficiently aroused to need to come off. She will be fully compensated by the thought that she has given you satisfaction, and if you gather her in your arms and whisper, 'We'll try again later,' she will fall asleep quite contentedly.

You may continue to have difficulties to a smaller or greater degree throughout the rest of your honeymoon, but as you grow accustomed to one another these difficulties will disappear.

One of these difficulties is premature ejaculation. There are two types of premature ejaculation, permanent and temporary. In the permanent type, the man *always* ejaculates his semen either before putting his penis into the vagina or within twenty seconds of entry. It was thought for a long time that this unhappy condition was a result of excessive masturbation in adolescence, but it is now known that this holds good for only a very small percentage of sufferers. In about 3 per cent of cases the cause is oversensitivity of the head of the penis in uncircumcised men, and by an abnormally short foreskin in about 2 per cent. In both these categories a cure can be effected by the very simple operation of circumcision. In the remaining 95 per cent of cases the causes are emotional, arising from such things as fear of sex, guilt feelings, anxiety, or a general lack of confidence usually based on the man's ungrounded fear that his penis is too small to be able to satisfy his mate. In all such cases the real treatment must be psychiatric therapy, which can be greatly helped by the application of one of the anaesthetic ointments I have just described.

Temporary premature ejaculation has been experienced at some time or another by all of us and is not an uncommon occurrence on the honeymoon. The cause is generally one or other of the following: abstention from lovemaking for a longish period, a terrific build-up in sexual tension, which can be physical or psychological in origin, or – and this applies particularly to younger men, especially in the early days of marriage – the result of a feeling of inexperience in lovemaking, or overexcitement arising out of anticipation among men who have had no heterosexual experience before marriage. Quite a large number of those married men who very occasionally indulge in lovemaking outside marriage also find that they are subject to premature ejaculation, even when they have no feelings of guilt, the cause being overexcitement brought on by the thought of the novelty of an untried partner.

130

Temporary premature ejaculation should cause you no anxiety at all. The best way to cope with it is to tell your wife that you are abnormally excited and that you ought to come quickly, at once, before you begin to make love properly. Either you can go into your wife – having taken good care to lubricate your penis well so as not to cause her discomfort in an unready vagina – or she can help you to come off with her hand. When you have achieved this relief, you can begin to make love to her, and within a quarter of an hour you will find that you can re-establish erection – if, indeed, you ever lost it – and from then on proceed to normal lovemaking which will be highly successful, more often than not, for both of you.

It is a sound rule during the first two or three months of marriage to avoid doing anything that might shock your bride. This holds good for every aspect of your sexual contacts. Gradually become bolder, but be always on the lookout for the smallest sign of diffidence, reluctance, or distaste and stop at once anything you may be doing. I personally believe that it takes a year before the average couple can begin to be sexually adventurous. Let your wife set the pace, and you will have nothing to fear.

10 THE WELL-MANNERED LOVER AND HIS WIFE'S MENSTRUATION

If the wedding night provides an outstanding opportunity for the lover to show how well-mannered he is, the period of his wife's menstruation provides yet another. There are very few men, especially if they have had sisters, who do not know that for several days before menstruation begins, a woman becomes irritable, short-tempered, and even more unpredictable than usual. If the husband has not learned this before marriage, it will not be long before he does.

Some women can be trying indeed during these days, and this is the time when bickering or quarrelling may take all the gilt off the romantic gingerbread. Nevertheless, it need not be at all like this if the husband shows sympathy and controls his own reactions to his wife's 'difficultness'. She will know she is being difficult and she will hate herself for it, but she cannot seem to help herself. The well-mannered lover realises this and in order to help him play his role of sympathiser and consoler, he will find out what it is that happens inside his wife's body that has this effect on her.

Every month the mucous lining of the womb prepares to receive a fertilised egg. The egg, which has matured in the ovary, begins to move into an adjoining organ called the Fallopian tube, and then gradually passes down the tube into the cavity of the womb. If, while in the Fallopian tube, the egg is fertilised by a sperm, it descends into the womb where it imbeds itself in the mucous lining and over the next nine months develops into a baby. If, however, it reaches the womb without being fertilised the mucous lining begins to detach itself, and taking the useless egg with it, passes out of the body via the vagina, in what is called menstruation. A new lining is then prepared by the womb ready for the next egg to come down from the ovaries.

The detachment of the mucous membrane from the walls of the womb causes an amount of blood to be released. This blood, which is shut off from the normal blood supply, is passed out of the body with the discarded lining and egg.

While this process is going on certain changes are taking place within the woman's body, affecting her production of the two female hormones so that they are for a time out of balance. It is this hormonal imbalance which creates the tensions that cause her out-of-sorts feeling, her swollen breasts and stomach, the tenderness of her nipples, her sometimes severe cramp pains, and above all the mental depression leading to irritability which she works off on those around her.

Though the average menstruating woman should never be treated as a sick woman, the physical pain and the mental depression are so severe in some women that they are actually ill. It is now possible to treat these extreme cases medically with a course of hormone pills which takes care of the hormone imbalance, so that the worst symptoms are reduced. The average woman, however, is not sick enough to need this treatment, yet her behaviour can often make life miserable for the family unless they are prepared to be sympathetic.

The well-mannered lover, therefore, understanding that she is in no way to blame for her irritability, while not treating her as an ill woman, will, during this period of anything between ten days and a week, show her particular little kindnesses. He will make up his mind never to be irritable himself, however much he may be irritated by what she says or does. He will not be affronted or force himself on her if she refuses all his sexual advances. He will do little, irksome chores which he does not normally do because they are done by her in the course of her housework. He will listen sympathetically to her moans and commiserate with and console her.

Such concrete signs of understanding can, and more often than not do, work as effectively as a course of hormone pills. She will appreciate them so much that she will make a determined effort to overcome her feelings of bad temper and her depression, and may even succeed.

133

It is well worth the effort, I assure you. Many a marriage that might have gone on the rocks has been firmly cemented because the husband treated his menstruating wife with consideration and love.

11 IMPOTENCE

Perhaps a man's greatest sexual fear is that he may lose his ability to have an erection, for apart from the fact that he cannot achieve coupling and orgasm without an erection, he judges his degree of manhood by his ability to satisfy his wife sexually, which he cannot do if he loses his erectile powers or cannot sustain an erection long enough to complete coupling in the normal way. This loss of erectile power is known as *impotence*, a term which is applied only to men.

As a man grows older, not only does his sex drive lose some of its frequency and strength, but his ability to achieve and sustain a strong erection is weakened slightly. It is when he notices this deterioration that he begins to fear the worst, though in ninety-nine cases out of a hundred his fears are groundless.

However, it is not only as a natural corollary to advancing age that a man's fear of impotence arises. It happens at some time or another that despite a terrific build-up of sexual tension, a man discovers that even under his wife's most skilful ministrations his penis just will not become erect. This is the man who has frightening visions of losing his virility, and it is for him that I have included this chapter, for what he does not realise is that there is probably not one of his married brothers who has not had a similar experience on more than one occasion.

Before I go on to describe why this temporary impotence occurs, I think I should point out that there are really serious types of impotence, serious because they are permanent until they are treated. This means that under no kind of stimulation whatsoever can a sufferer at any time have an erection, that he is to all intents and purposes sexually dead. Moreover, I must most strongly urge any of my readers who finds himself a victim of this condition not to lose a single moment in consulting his doctor, for his impotence may be of a type – psychogenic impotence, especially – which can be completely cured by treatment.

The temporary impotence and the loss of erectile powers as a result of advancing age are what I am most concerned with here. The first may arise from a variety of causes, such as overindulgence in smoking, the effect of a narcotic drug given in the course of treatment or taken accidentally or deliberately, or drinking too much, and numerous other causes of this kind, either mental or physical, though, perhaps strangely, fatigue of either kind does not usually induce impotence though it may impair the strength of the erection.

Even if you experience such temporary impotence on two or three successive occasions, do not become worried or afraid that you are in danger of becoming permanently impotent. If you do you are setting up a barrier to recovery. What you must do is to think over what you have been doing lately and try to determine whether any of the causes I have mentioned could apply. But whether they do or do not, the cure is a healthy diet and a good dose of fresh air.

One type of temporary impotence, which some men find mildly frightening, is what one might term demi-impotence. You begin to make love and have a really strong erection. Normally you would be able to maintain this erection right through to orgasm and perhaps beyond, but suddenly you realise that your wife is caressing your fully limp penis. When this does occur, though she will be able to produce an erection strong enough to allow you to go into her, it will not be a really strong erection, though this will not prevent you from coming off with quite intense sensations. This is nothing to worry about either.

If you think it over calmly I believe you will come to the conclusion that perhaps you were tired or that subconsciously you were wishing that your wife would administer some out-of-the-ordinary stimulation to the penis itself, maybe a really hard squeeze of the shaft when she was trying to stimulate the frenum with light touches, or that she would give you really vigorous mouth-genital caresses when she was administering rather colourless caresses with her fingers. If you were tired, the strain placed on your nervous system may have been too great for it to organise the special flow of blood to the cavernous bodies of the penis to bring about erection. Rest and relaxation will obviate this, but in any

136

case you surely have nothing to worry about, because you did after all achieve relief of tension through coming off.

The case of age affecting the strength of the erection is somewhat different, because here the cause of the loss of strength is what is known as reflex erection instead of cerebral erection, which is the type of erection young men normally have. Cerebral erection results largely from impulses passing downward from the brain to the lower centres of the spinal cord in the erection centre. This type of erection may persist into old age, but in middle life or later the speed with which it occurs is lessened. When this happens usually reflex erection takes over.

Reflex erection is erection which results from the reflex action of the erectile nerves to touch. In the man whose erection is of the cerebral type, the penis reacts very quickly to touch, for touch is an added stimulant to the stimulus of the brain. The reflex erection, however, results solely from touch, and requires a varying amount of massage of the penis, preferably by the wife. Earlier, it may take from two or three to five to ten minutes of slow massage; but as you get older the period of massage grows longer, though erection will definitely come.

It is because so many men do not know that there is such a thing as reflex erection, that is, erection that can only be brought about by massage, that they believe themselves to be impotent and accept their impotence, when they could and would respond very satisfactorily to massage. Certainly, if they are capable of 'morning erections' they are capable of erection for lovemaking, for the 'morning erection' proves that the erectile mechanism is still functioning.

So do stop worrying about becoming impotent! Only a very few types of impotence are incurable. Certainly temporary impotence and the apparent, though not real, impotence of aging are nothing to be frightened of, for they are either passing phases in your sexual experience, or only need the right kind of stimulus to overcome them.

But if you do become worried, for heaven's sake lose no time in consulting your doctor. If you are absolutely frank with him, he will soon straighten you out. The vast majority of impotent men are only impotent because they cannot bring themselves to reveal even to their doctors that they seem to have lost their virility. In no other circumstances of life can a man be more stupid.

12   OBJECTIVE ACHIEVED?

In the first chapter of this book I wrote, 'My objective in writing
this book is to do for husbands what I have done for wives in
Mainly for Wives. That is to say, I want to lift the husband's response to sex from lust – the satisfying of a purely physical urge
in the shortest possible time by the most direct methods – to love,
the using of physical sex to express a spiritual urge.'

If you have read so far I hope you will be able to say that I have
achieved my object, if not wholly, at least in large part. I hope you
have found in these pages answers to some of the questions that
you may have been asking yourself for a long time. I think I may
justifiably claim that I have been more frank and detailed in my
descriptions than the great majority of other writers on the subject.
Nevertheless, I am only too aware that I have by no means been
exhaustive. To be exhaustive would require a collection of books
the size of the *Encyclopaedia Britannica*, for example, but in any
case, response to the sexual drive is such an individual thing that,
in my view, a couple should teach themselves as much as they can
by their own explorations and experiments. For them to be
successful in their experiments they need, of course, a certain basic
knowledge, and I hope that I have provided this basic knowledge for the husband in this book.

My aim, as I am sure you will have spotted by this time, has been
to help you to become not only a skilful lover, but what I have
called a well-mannered lover. A man may be highly skilled in the
whole technique of love, and yet be a sexual bully and a bore. If he
is a sexual bully, then he will not be a lover – one who uses sex to
express his love for his partner. It is the consideration one shows
for one's partner – that is, being sexually well-mannered – that is

the major requirement for the achievement of a complete, happy, and satisfying sexual relationship, which in its turn is an essential major contribution towards the achievement of a complete totally happy, and entirely satisfying marriage relationship.

INDEX

age, effect of on sexual drive, 53–54, 103–104
American tip. *See* Malthus cap
appreciation, spoken, 107
average-sexed individuals, 46, 47, 49, 50, 51, 59, 60, 61, 63, 64

Bartholin glands, 40–41, 93
birth control, 92–100, 105, 106
boredom. *See* lovemaking, monotony in
breasts, woman's, 39, 77
  See also nipples

capacity, sexual. *See* sexual capacity
caresses, various, 29, 41–42, 66, 110–111, 116, 126
  See also kissing; stimulation
cavernous bodies, 18–20
cervical cap, 98–99
cervix, 35, 36
circumcision, 21, 22, 102, 130
cleanliness, importance of, 106
climax
  female, 10, 63
  male, 10, 21, 63
    See also orgasm
clitoris, 38–40
  See also coupling, technique of
coitus interruptus, 92, 93–94
coming. *See* orgasm
coming off

female, 50
male, 50
  See also intercourse
communication during lovemaking, 7, 108–109
conception, 9
condom, 95–96, 97, 127
contraceptive pill, 93, 100
control, acquiring, 87–88, 100–104, 117
corpora cavernosa, 18
coupling, 40, 52
  substitute for, 94
  technique of, 66–91, 121
    See also wedding night, the
Cowper's glands, 24–25, 93, 111

desire
  contrasts in, 63–65
  frequency of, 47
  off-the-beaten-track, 109
diaphragm (Dutch cap), 97–100, 127
divorce, 10
drive, sex. *See* sex drive
Dutch cap. *See* diaphragm

ejaculation, premature, 102–103, 129, 130–131
epididymis, 24
erection, female, 9, 43–45, 119
erection, male, 9, 20, 25–26, 30–34
  automatic, 32, 46

induced, 29–30
mechanical, 33–34
types of, 32–34
See also impotence
erection centre, 70, 82
erector nerves, 29
erogenous zones, 58, 60, 72, 83, 116
man's, 29
woman's, 41–42
erotic images, 45

foreplay. *See* love-play
foreskin, 20–22
frenum (frenulum), 21, 22, 27, 116
frequency, 54, 63
frigidity, 92, 94, 107

glans, 20
guilt, feelings of, 8, 16

heavy petting, 94
highly sexed individuals, 46, 47, 48, 49–51, 53, 59, 60, 61, 63, 64
hymen, breaking of, 124, 125–126, 127–129

ignorance, women's sexual. *See* sexual ignorance
impotence
permanent, 135
psychogenic, 136
temporary, 32, 135–137
intercourse, 9, 66–91
psychological aspects of, 14
purpose of, 15

kissing, 70, 81, 117
deep, 69, 72, 81

love, relationship between sex and, 15, 16
lovemaking
during menstruation, 122

frequency of, 121
monotony in, 66–67
morning, 120–121
nothing unnatural in, 8, 52, 85
sleep after, 59
successful, 13, 92–104
technique of, 105–122
vocabulary of, 108–109
love-play (foreplay), 60, 66, 86–87, 105
See also stimulation
lover, well-mannered, 107–122
on the wedding night, 123–131
and wife's menstruation period, 132–134
low-sexed individuals, 47, 48, 49, 51, 63
lubrication, 40–41, 93
See also Bartholin glands; Cowper's glands

Malthus cap (American tip), 96
masturbation, 56
female, 39
male, 32, 54, 64, 129, 130
medium-sexed individuals. *See* average-sexed individuals
menstruation period, 64, 94–95
attitude of husband toward wife's, 132–134
lovemaking during, 122
modesty, wife's, 126
See also reluctance
Mount of Venus, 41, 42
movements, variations of, in coupling, 85–86, 87

nakedness, desirability of, in love-play, 105–106
nipples
female, 44, 60, 69, 77, 81, 115
male, 29, 70, 77, 78

ointments to aid premature ejaculation, 102–103

141

orgasm, 11, 18, 49–51, 56–65, 87
    female, 9, 11, 39–40, 42, 58, 88–90
    responsibility for, 7
    simultaneous, 63, 89–90
ovaries, 36–37

penetration, 71–77, 83, 84
penis
    functioning of, 24
    movement of, 69–70, 83, 87
    size of, 7, 25–26
    structure of, 18–22, 27–29
    See also coupling
performance, sexual. *See* sexual performance
pessaries, 97–98
pillow, use of, in coupling, 70, 72, 74, 80, 84, 128
'plug', 42
point-of-no-return, 56, 60, 71, 78, 88, 101, 118
positions during intercourse. *See* coupling, technique of
pregnancy, fear of, 92, 93, 100
prepuce. *See* foreskin
psychological attitudes, 7, 14, 45, 64–65, 71, 101, 127

reluctance, 63–65
    See also modesty
response, sexual, 11, 46–55
Rhythm Method, 92, 94–95

Safe Period, 92, 94–95
scrotum, 17, 18, 22–23
    pressure on, 34
semen, 9, 14, 24, 58, 59, 93
seminal vesicle, 24
sensations resulting from inter-course, 16, 18, 54–55, 56–58, 62, 69, 78–79, 86–88
    man's, 10, 51, 54–55, 77
    woman's, 10, 51, 77
    See also orgasm

sex
    ideas concerning, 9–12
    individual response to, 46–55
    male attitude toward, 10–12, 14
    moral attitude toward, 15, 52
    practical, 9, 15
sex act
    performance of, 14
    woman's role in, 11–12, 111–113
    naturalness of, 16
sex drive, 48, 53, 65, 103–104
    effect of age on, 54, 103–104
sex life, shared responsibility for, 11
sex manuals, 8, 12–13, 31, 41
sexual capacity, 8, 53–54, 103–104
sexual equipment
    female, 35–45
    male, 16–34
sexual ignorance, women's, 9–10
sexual nervous system, 27–29, 41–42
    female, 77–78
    male, 77–78
sexual performance, 52–55
sexual tension, 48, 56, 59, 79, 88, 103
    build-up of, 56, 70
    relief of, 59, 62, 89
sleep after lovemaking, 59
smegma, 21
sounds, stimulating effect of, 118
sperm, 22–24, 93, 94
spermicides, 93, 97–99
spongy body, 18, 20
stimulation, 9, 29, 32, 33, 39, 41, 43, 54, 56, 60, 63, 78, 102
    techniques of, 62, 66, 89, 112–119, 136, 137

tension, sexual. *See* sexual tension
terminology, limitations of, in discussing sex, 13
testicles, 18, 22–24
tongue, use of in love-play, 29, 42, 69, 81, 83, 116

urethra, 18, 24, 58
  female, 38
  male, 18, 24

vagina, 35, 38–39, 58, 128–130
  construction of, 44
  size of, 36
    See also coupling
vas deferens, 24

vocabulary of lovemaking, 108–109

wedding night, the, 123–131
wet dream, 33
womb, 36, 37
  development of baby in, 38

NEL BESTSELLERS

ROBERT HEINLEIN
☐ 04675 3   The Number of the Beast   £2.95
☐ 00403 1   Stranger In A Strange Land   £2.75

IRWIN SHAW
☐ 05024 6   The Top Of The Hill   £2.95
☐ 02089 4   Rich Man, Poor Man   £2.95

HAROLD ROBBINS
☐ 04981 7   Memories Of Another Day   £2.95
☐ 00674 3   The Inheritors   £2.95

STEPHEN KING
☐ 04552 8   The Stand   £1.95
☐ 02517 9   Carrie   £3.50

All these books are available at your local bookshop or newsagent, or can be ordered direct from the publisher. Just tick the titles you want and fill in the form below.

Prices and availability subject to change without notice.

Hodder & Stoughton Paperbacks, P.O. BOX 11, Falmouth, Cornwall

Please send cheque or postal order, and allow the following for postage and packing:

U.K. – 55p for one book, plus 22p for the second book, and 14p for each additional book ordered up to £1.75 maximum.

B.F.P.O. and EIRE – 55p for the first book, plus 22p for the second book, and 14p per copy for the next 7 books, 8p per book thereafter.

OTHER OVERSEAS CUSTOMERS – £1.00 for the first book, plus 25p per copy for each additional book.

Name ....

Address ....

....